# MIKKI LISH & KELLY NGAI

# The Spellbound Tree

A HOARDER HiLL Adventure

**Chicken House**

2 PALMER STREET,
FROME, SOMERSET
BA11 1DS

Text © Mikki Lish & Kelly Ngai 2022
Cover illustration © Maxine Lee-Mackie 2022

First published in Great Britain in 2022
Chicken House
2 Palmer Street
Frome, Somerset BA11 1DS
United Kingdom
www.chickenhousebooks.com

Chicken House/Scholastic Ireland, 89E Lagan Road, Dublin Industrial Estate,
Glasnevin, Dublin D11 HP5F, Republic of Ireland

Mikki Lish & Kelly Ngai have asserted their right under the Copyright, Designs
and Patents Act 1988 to be identified as the authors of this work.

Cover and interior design by Steve Wells

Printed and                                                          4YY

British Library Cataloguing in Publication data available.

PB ISBN 978-1-913322-57-1
eISBN 978-1-913696-79-5

*To Doug Ngai – the original bear, brother
and friend who introduced us.*

*To Mikki, for all the wild ideas and belief in us.
And to my parents, Juliana and Michael Ngai,
for everything they do, great and small – K. N.*

*For changing the course of my life:
The Holland family for their support,
friendship and amazing talents.
Mitch Rose for making THE introduction.
And especially Kelly Ngai for being 'Superman' to my
Clark Kent. I am forever thankful – M. L.*

## CHAPTER 1

## THEY ARE NOT THEMSELVES

Hedy van Beer looked up from her book. The garage doors had exploded open and what looked like a huge cloud billowed out in a puff. There was no way her brother, Spencer, had planned whatever had just happened.

Fearing the worst, Hedy tucked her book into her waistband. A knotted rope hung from the sycamore tree where she had been reading, letting her scrunch and stretch her way to the ground like a cross between a monkey and a caterpillar.

'Spencer?' she yelled, sprinting for the garage.

Spencer and their cousins, Jelly and Max, stumbled out through the ballooning cloud into the garden. They were all a little damp, as though they'd walked through mist.

'What happened?' Hedy asked. Spencer was trying out a device that he'd been given by their friend, Mrs Pal. It was an artefact from Iceland called a skyskepnur, roughly translated as 'sky creature'. It was supposed to create massive cloud shapes.

'It was going all right,' said Spencer, 'until Jelly tried to make a woolly mammoth the actual size of a woolly mammoth.'

Jelly rolled her eyes. 'What's the point of making a woolly mammoth if it's not *mammoth*?' She added to Hedy, 'Mine grew bigger than a hippo. The biggest any of the boys' cloud animals got was our cat.'

'You can't say Spencer's cat cloud failed since it was cat-sized,' said Max. He pulled his make-believe goggles from his head. They were fashioned from toilet rolls and a yellow elastic band and had left two distinct indentations around his eyes.

'Yeah, but a cat-sized cat isn't going to carry us very far,' said Jelly.

'An exploding mammoth won't get you much

further,' Hedy said.

'What do you care?' said Spencer, exasperated. 'You don't want to go anywhere or do anything these days.'

'That's not true,' she burst out. But the look the others gave her told a different story, that she was the wettest of wet blankets these days.

Spencer backed away from the cloud that was still puffing from the garage. 'So how did you do it, Jelly? Did Grandpa John tell you something when you had your secret meeting with him?'

'I keep telling you, it wasn't that secret,' Jelly insisted. 'It was something for school. Ask my mum, she was there.'

'What does Grandpa John have to do with your school though?' Hedy asked.

Jelly began dancing around the driveway to break up the mist. 'It's just a sort of recommendation thing.'

The explanation didn't add up. Jelly and her mum, Toni, had been chatting with Grandpa John too long for it to be a simple recommendation. It nagged at Hedy for a reason she couldn't put her finger on.

'Look, I know he's *your* grandad,' Jelly added. 'You don't have to be jealous that I'm trying to steal him away from you or anything.'

'We're not jealous,' said Hedy, but she knew she sounded defensive and whiney. Despite Jelly's off-handed way of saying almost everything that came into her head, she could be very perceptive at times.

'Oh no,' grumbled Max. 'The elastic on my magic goggles broke.'

'Here.' Hedy held out her hand to inspect them. 'Easy-peasy. A couple of staples, it'll be fine.'

'Can you fix it for me, Hedy?'

'What do they do again?'

'Well . . .' Max bit his lip, thinking on the spot. 'They're my Shadow of Magic goggles. They show the magic all around you.'

Hedy brought the goggles to her eyes, playing along. There was nothing to see but the garden of course. 'I guess these do need fixing cos I can't see anything. It'll cost you.'

'I can pay you five grotesque poops.'

Hedy made a gagging face. 'I'll do it for free then.'

When the cloud cleared, the four of them went back into the garage.

In days gone by, the skyskepnur had created steeds for riders through the sky. It was not in perfect working order though, so Mrs Pal had tasked Spencer with fixing it. She knew that Spencer wanted to become a maker like her, someone who could craft objects with special enchanted powers, and she was subtly starting his informal apprenticeship.

Spencer picked up the skyskepnur, which looked like a cross between a fishing rod and a butterfly-catcher. There was a net at the top of a long rod, and halfway down the rod was a leather bulb for water and a small handle. Unfortunately, the bulb had a couple of punctures from which water leaked at random moments, and nothing Spencer had used to fix the holes had stuck.

He began waving it through the air whilst winding the handle and muttering to himself.

'Your shoes are going to get wet,' Hedy noted as water dribbled from the bulb.

Spencer ignored her. Soon, a small mist formed in the net. When he quickly swiped the net downwards the mist detached and became a tiny cloud in the shape of a rhinoceros.

'That's even smaller than before!' Max complained.

Spencer sighed. 'I know. I'm sure I fixed the handle, but there's still something wrong with the bulb. It won't stop leaking.'

The perfectly formed rhinoceros began to gallop in the air, looping around Hedy. As it moved, it began to change shape just as real clouds did, and a minute later it had re-formed as a pig. But soon after that, the trotting pig cloud began to slow down and then disintegrate, becoming shapeless and then disappearing altogether.

'I can't work out how to make the clouds bigger and stay for longer,' said Spencer. 'How could anyone ride them if they disappear so fast?' He held the rod out to Hedy. 'Want to try?'

'No thanks,' she said.

'Why not?' demanded Max. He refused to accept that anyone would pass up a chance to use magical artefacts. 'It's only *clouds*. You couldn't kill anyone with a cloud, they're harmless.'

'Don't be such an insensitive twerp, Max,' Jelly hissed. 'Uncle John only got out of hospital a month ago.'

A couple of months back, Grandpa John had taken ill in the woods. Or rather, he'd tried to use magic while in the woods with Hedy and Spencer, to cure the illness he already knew he had. The magic hadn't worked though. It had backfired and his illness had taken a sudden, terrible turn for the worse, right there among the trees. Hedy's frightened run back to the house for help, the ambulance taking him away – they were things she didn't think she would ever forget.

She turned on her heels and marched out. 'Don't forget,' she said over her shoulder, 'if the clouds are big enough to ride, they're big enough to fall off.'

She wasn't in the mood to talk now, but they followed her out of the garage anyway. Before long, little round grey stones dropped on to their heads. They looked up. It was one of the grotesques, the gargoyle. She was one of the more fearsome stone statues from the roof: her wings spanned nearly a metre, her haunches were muscled, and below the horns on her head were sharp eyes that missed very little.

Max dropped to the ground, eagerly gathering the pebbles.

'Really, Tempest?' said Hedy. 'You know, you can just say *hi* instead of dropping your poop on us.'

'You cannot deny that you pay more attention to us this way,' said Tempest in her raspy voice, swooping to the ground. 'What were you doing?'

They told the gargoyle about their feeble attempts to use the skyskepnur.

She sniffed and flared her wings. 'I am not much

surprised that it is not working as you expect. There is something I must show you. Come, meet me on the roof.'

At the top of Grandpa John's house was the belvedere, an open-sided tower with an excellent view of the area. Tempest, of course, could simply fly up to the roof from the garden, so by the time the children had climbed three flights of stairs and come out through the attic, she was bobbing her head impatiently.

'Look at that,' she said with disgust, jutting her chin at her fellow grotesques. They were clustered in twos and threes murmuring quietly between themselves. All of them ignored the couple of squirrels that scampered across the slate tiles, and birds were swooping freely around the roof. The gryphon grotesque even had a sparrow sitting on its shoulder.

'What's happening?' Hedy asked.

'They're not guarding!' Tempest exclaimed. 'They should be shooing all these intruders away! Who knows who those squirrels are working for, or what secrets that sparrow is trying to find out with its wittering?'

Jelly leant closer, grinning. 'Why? What have the squirrels said that makes you suspicious?'

Tempest didn't realize she was being made fun of. 'Well nothing, because ordinarily I move them on without delay. Their persistence in returning alarms me. The real problem, however, is that the other grotesques are not suspicious at all! It is in our very nature to be wary and to . . . to *guard*. That is the purpose given to us. But lately, they are changed. They are not themselves. This is no better than a tea party!'

*That's the problem*, Hedy realized. Except for Tempest, the grotesques weren't the vigilant, growling creatures that had chased her from the roof a few years ago.

She scanned the roof until her eyes fell upon the small statue of a raven at the far edge. 'I haven't seen the raven in a while. Has she changed?'

'Indeed, Hedy, she has changed because she has *not*. She has not transformed into her feathered form for some time. It is as though she is nothing more than a plain carving, but we all know that is not true.'

'What are you saying?' Spencer asked. 'Are the grotesques and the raven sick?'

Tempest scowled. 'There is something going wrong with magic.'

## CHAPTER 2

## THE NURSE AND THE NEIGHBOUR

The four children decided to look for Grandpa John to relay what Tempest had told them, but unexpectedly found that while they'd been talking outside, he had come up to the attic already, with business of his own. He was deep in thought, muttering crossly to himself.

'What's wrong?' Hedy asked, as her eyes readjusted to the dimmer light inside.

'This intractable thing is what's wrong,' said Grandpa John, jerking a hand at Sir Roland, an enchanted suit of armour who guarded the attic.

'What's he done?' Spencer asked.

Grandpa John was suddenly racked by a bout of coughing that made Hedy's stomach clench.

'Defiance and insubordination,' he grunted when he caught his breath. 'I need his sword but the blasted tin can isn't handing it over, never mind that I'm its master. I was hoping to have it done before Bess turns up.'

Hedy shared an excited look with the others. Bess was a treasure hunter they'd got to know on their last adventure, and in fact the very person who had lent Hedy the book that she'd been reading earlier. 'What's Bess coming over for?'

'He and I will take a little trip soon.'

'To where?'

But Grandpa John didn't answer, concentrating on Sir Roland again. He reached for the steel gauntlet that held the sword. The suit of armour immediately raised its arm, swinging it this way and that in the air out of Grandpa John's grasp, like a bully teasing a smaller child. Jelly had to nudge Max to stop him giggling.

'Grandpa,' said Hedy. 'Tempest thinks there's something wrong with magic.'

Grandpa John didn't seem surprised at all. 'Does she?'

As he twisted to grab the gauntlet, a small notebook fell out of his pocket. This time, Sir Roland moved, plunging his sword point down and pinning the notebook to the floor before Grandpa John could pick it up.

'Scoundrel!' snapped Grandpa John. 'Release that.'

Sir Roland ignored him. Nothing that Grandpa John said or did made the obstinate suit of armour move an inch.

'Is your trip with Bess something to do with magic going wrong?' Hedy asked.

'No comment, my dear girl.' Exactly what he had said the last twenty times Hedy had questioned him too closely.

She pulled her book from her waistband and ran a hand over its embossed leather cover. Forty years old, it was a factual account of another treasure hunter's search for a powerful artefact in Guatemala. These sorts of books couldn't be found in a regular library, for magic was supposed to be kept secret from the wider world.

But this was the last book about treasure she would

borrow, Hedy had decided. There was no point reading about magical objects if she was never going to use
them. Magic was dangerous even before there was
something wrong with it. Who could blame her for
wanting to swear off it?

That didn't mean the detective in her couldn't use
the book another way, though.

'Should I give Bess his book back when he gets
here?' she asked. 'Or will he stop by again when you
come home?'

'Probably best to return it to him when he arrives,'
said Grandpa John.

*So*, Hedy thought, *Grandpa John and Bess are
going to part ways once they've done whatever they need
to do.*

'Can't you give us a clue to where you're going,
Grandpa John?' Spencer pleaded.

The doorbell rang and Grandpa John smiled,
relieved. 'Thank goodness Lark is here to save me from
your nosiness.'

Grandpa John had to take the stairs more slowly
than he used to, so Hedy darted downstairs to answer
the door.

Waiting on the porch was Lark, a carer who

checked on Grandpa John three times a week since his return from hospital. She was a little older than Mum, but younger than Grandma Rose, with brown bobbed hair and a pixie-like face. Whatever the weather, Lark always wore a cardigan, pinned at the chest with the same wooden brooch – a tree with red berries.

'Hello, Hedy,' said Lark with her bright smile. 'I hope your grandad hasn't run off just because I'm here to check on him.'

Hedy grinned back. 'He's coming down from the attic, so he might be a minute.' When Lark checked her watch, Hedy added, 'Is it making you late for something?'

Lark shook her head. 'Your grandad is my only one today. How is he?'

'He's a bit grumpy about something,' said Hedy, 'so don't take it personally if he . . . grumps.'

'Oh, I'm used to that now. I find it funny, really. What's he grumpy about? Not you kids, I bet. That usually makes him chirpy as anything.' Lark looked into the hallway. 'Is your whole family here?'

Hedy sat on the porch steps and Lark joined her. 'Just me, Spence, Jelly and Max. All our parents and Grandma Rose and my Uncle Peter are at the British

Museum. Some things my parents helped discover are in a new exhibition there, so there's an opening event this afternoon.'

Lark made an *oooh* face. 'Sounds fancy. Will they be back soon?'

'Not until after dinner.' After a moment, Hedy said quietly, 'Grandpa John's planning a trip.'

'In his condition? Where to?'

'He won't tell us. But no one wants him to travel. My grandma isn't happy about it. Actually, I think she wanted us here so he couldn't run away and ask forgiveness later.'

'What's so important?'

'I think it's connected to what he used to do for work.'

'Oh,' said Lark, 'magician-y things.'

The way Lark said it, it was as though she knew all about real magic. Hedy had to remind herself that, as far as Lark was supposed to know, Grandpa John was a retired stage magician, an illusionist. She wouldn't know about his ability to do real magic.

Lark's next words took Hedy by surprise. 'He *should* go, I think.'

'That's the exact opposite of what I thought you'd say.'

'He's very sharp, your grandad,' said Lark. 'I'm sure he knows how to take precautions. When you have a calling, it can be hard to give it up. Especially if you're good at it.'

'Do you have one? A calling?' Hedy asked, intrigued by her tone. 'What was it?'

Lark hesitated. 'Dance. But I was injured. I'd dedicated so much of my life to it and then I couldn't do it any more.'

With Lark's petite frame, Hedy could easily picture her as a dancer. 'You're a nurse now – isn't that a calling?'

'It's a calling for some,' said Lark.

*But not yours*, Hedy guessed. 'Can you teach dance?'

'To be honest, it would make me feel too sad that I can't do it nowadays. So, I understand why your grandad won't give this up, whatever it is. Is he going on this trip alone?'

'With a friend of ours. I think that's the only thing stopping Grandma Rose from tying him to a chair.'

'Hello, Lark!' Grandpa John called out, having made it to the ground floor at last. 'Time for the blood pressure and medication nonsense, is it?'

Lark scrambled to her feet. 'Wall-to-wall nonsense coming right up, John.'

'Spence! Pass!' Jelly called, waving her arm.

Spencer's football, almost magically, was never far from reach. It wasn't long before the rest of them were drawn into the game in the front garden, shouting and laughing as they ran around in the midday sun.

But misfortune struck. Jelly let fly a ball that Spencer should have blocked, but Max tripped over his own feet, and knocked Spencer to the ground. The ball sailed over the hedge into the next-door garden.

They all froze. A moment later, they heard the faint sound of the neighbour's front door being unlatched.

'Mr Grutz?' Spencer asked.

'Hate his guts,' Max finished under his breath.

Mr Grutz had moved into the house next door a few months ago. He was standoffish, bordering on surly, and none of the children liked him. Grandma Rose had reminded them, 'Don't forget, John was the grumpy recluse of the village too. Don't rush to judgement.'

'But he's weird and so nosy!' Spencer had said. 'We saw him snooping around in your postbox by the gate.'

'He spies through the hedges too,' Hedy had added. 'He thinks he's super subtle about it. But no one could do *that* much gardening and still have such a pathetic-looking garden.'

One weekend, they'd painted a sign that said *Hello, Mr Grutz!* and stuck it near the hedge. Jelly had gone a step further. Her sign had read, *What are you looking at, Stickybeak?*

'He could only be offended if he actually saw it,' she'd tried to explain to a very disapproving Grandma Rose, 'which would mean he was spying and deserved it.'

Now, knowing Mr Grutz was coming out, Max edged away. 'Do we make a run for it?'

'Don't be silly,' said Hedy. 'We didn't do anything wrong.'

'This time,' muttered Spencer. 'Jelly, you have to ask for the ball back.'

'Why me?' Jelly protested.

'Cos you kicked it!'

'*You* were supposed to block it. You go ask for it.'

'I would've had it if Max hadn't fallen on to me.'

Both Spencer and Jelly turned to Max and said, 'Max, *you* go ask for it.' But he shook his head. Nothing short of a bulldozer would have made him budge.

Hedy rolled her eyes and strode towards the hedge as Mr Grutz appeared at the gate. He was a tall man who hunched his shoulders as though ashamed of his height, and he was wearing his usual corduroy jacket, once red but now quite faded.

The pointy top of Mr Grutz's head was bald but wiry hair hung on tenaciously around the ears, trying to meet up with his unkempt beard. Jelly had rather unkindly said his head looked like an egg that tried to grow hair but got bored halfway through. The image stuck in Hedy's mind and chose this moment to make a giggle bubble up in her chest.

Mr Grutz looked at Hedy, then held out the ball. 'This yours?'

Hedy tried to swallow the nervous giggle down. 'It's my brother's.'

'You could've broken one of my windows.'

*But we didn't*, she wanted to say. 'We didn't mean to kick it over there. We'll be more careful from now on.'

Mr Grutz's eyes narrowed. 'Might be easier to be careful if you didn't have the ball at all.' He ran his eyes over Grandpa John's house. 'Might stop you breaking one of your grandparents' windows too.'

Hedy lost all urge to laugh. Was Mr Grutz seriously

trying to confiscate Spencer's football? 'We won't kick it out here any more,' she said finally.

Mr Grutz lobbed the ball over the gate.

'Thank you,' said Hedy stiffly.

With a sound that was somewhere between a grunt and a growl, Mr Grutz turned and went back inside.

As they retreated to the back garden, whispering indignantly, Tempest circled down from above in a rush of air.

'I saw you speaking with that man,' she said. 'Beware. He observes too much. He is no ordinary prying neighbour.'

## CHAPTER 3

## THE SNOW GLOBES

'Can't you fly over him and poop on *his* head?' said Max.

That earned a gruff chuckle from the gargoyle. 'In truth, that would be greatly satisfying. But it would go against the Master's wishes.'

'If Greedy Grutz isn't your garden variety busybody, what is he?' Jelly wondered.

'And what are we going to do about it?' said Spencer. 'I bet he wants something in the house.'

'I wish Uncle John would turn Greedy Grutz into an actual boiled egg,' said Jelly. 'You know, bend his rule against using magic just once for the most annoying man in the world.'

'*We* should magic something together to get back at Greedy Grutz,' said Spencer.

'Like a miniature cloud rhino?' Jelly scoffed.

Spencer pursed his lips. 'Something scarier.'

'We're bogs, remember,' said Hedy. 'Bog standard. *No* magical gifts.'

Jelly pulled an outraged face. 'Geez, no need to be so bitter!'

'I'm not being bitter. It's the truth.'

'But you're totally skipping the part about how we're awesome adventurers,' said Jelly.

'The Awesome Adventurers' Association,' said Spencer. 'We could have membership badges and stuff.'

'Exactly, Spence. Lame name, but I'd join anyway,' said Jelly. 'Hedy would be the president and you'd be the . . . gadgets guy?'

'But Spencer's gadgets don't work,' said Max.

Spencer huffed. 'They will, one day. I'll turn making into an invincible blend of science and engineering and magic.'

As they dreamt up absurd, grandiose plans for the

association, Hedy began to feel an odd tugging sensation in the air. She peered around.

Dried leaves skittered across the lawn. Everything dimmed. A split second later, an illogical patch of midnight spread over them: the house, the garden of Hoarder Hill, right up to its fence line.

Hedy could only manage a single word, 'What—' before they were all stunned senseless by shock waves from inside. As her head hit the ground, every thought shattered and her mind went dark.

'Hello?' said a voice.

Hedy's eyelids refused to open.

But the voice persisted. 'Hello? Wake up. Wake up, Hedy.' Something cool and hard doggedly nudged her shoulder. 'Come along now. Spencer. Jelly? Max?'

With a grunt, Hedy opened her eyes the tiniest sliver. She and the others were on the ground, slumped over each other like puppies. They showed no signs of stirring.

There was another nudge. 'Ow,' Hedy mumbled. 'You got me with your horns, Tempest.'

The gargoyle drew back. 'They do come in useful on occasion. Are you well? Can you stand?'

'Give me a week and I could.' Hedy desperately wanted to close her eyes again.

Tempest prodded Hedy once more. 'You do not have a week. I fear you do not have even a day to lose.'

'Why?'

'You have been out to the world for nearly an hour. And no one has come looking for you. There has been no hue or cry from inside the house. What does that mean for the Master?'

Hedy rolled to her side, eased herself from under Max's leg and eventually on to her feet. She felt wobbly.

It still looked like night over Hoarder Hill. Beyond the gate and fence, however, it seemed to be late afternoon. Although the sun didn't shine on her, she could see it hanging over the western horizon, indifferent to the nightfall over them. But there was no crowd of people staring at the dome of darkness over Grandpa John's house. Was it invisible from the other side?

Hedy spotted an arrow-shaped flock of birds flying from Foxwood towards Hoarder Hill. But as they approached, they soared around the dome, as though a mountain peak was in their way, and then they corrected their path on the other side. The birds had sensed they could not fly through the darkened space, whatever it was.

'I checked the roof,' Tempest informed Hedy. 'The other grotesques are even less themselves than before.'

'And how do you feel?'

The gargoyle twisted her long neck to look herself over. 'As I ever did.' But there was a shade of doubt in her voice.

Steadier now, Hedy tried to rouse the others but none of them so much as fluttered their eyelids. She needed help. 'Can you watch over them?' she asked Tempest. 'I'll go check on Grandpa John.'

Tempest splayed her wings. 'Go. I shall guard.'

Hedy shuffled to the back door and eased it open. The kitchen was empty, as was the laundry room.

Grandpa John had been with Lark in the lounge, but when Hedy got there, it too was empty. The only thing moving was Grandpa John's small figurine of a Roman charioteer, hurtling in magical circuits through the air. When Hedy caught him and his horses, she listened for the sound she had heard whenever she held him – the clamour of a great arena crowd and the thunder of horses' hooves. But she heard nothing. There was only a sharp snap as the charioteer flicked his small whip to be freed, so that he could continue his mysterious, lonely race.

Dread coiled like a snake in her belly. She walked through the house, and found the door to Grandpa John's study wide open. He never left it like that.

'Grandpa?' Hedy called out. She sounded faint and childlike in the silence blanketing the house. She couldn't see them in here either. But Grandpa John's wand lay at the edge of his desk. It was very odd that it should be out at all because he hardly ever used it. The last time that he had, he'd collapsed in the woods. The wand lay at an odd angle – an angle that told Hedy it had not been neatly placed there. It had been dropped. She circled the desk to take a closer look and choked on her breath.

On the floor was a snow globe, with nothing in it but tiny white flakes and the miniature form of a sleeping man.

It was Grandpa John.

Hedy dropped to her knees and picked it up, making the snow inside drift and dance. 'Grandpa John!' He rolled over on to his back, but didn't open his eyes. Shouting his name made no difference. She wondered if he could even hear her. The inflatable velcro sleeve that Lark used to measure his blood pressure was still on his arm.

Out of the corner of her eye, she spotted another snow globe that had rolled under the desk. She reached for it. Asleep inside this one was Lark.

*Stop shaking*, Hedy told herself as she got to her feet and placed the snow globes on the desk. She tried not to think what would happen if her trembling hands were to drop one of them and break the glass. They were immersed in water like figurines in any other snow globe, making Lark's hair waft like seagrass. But at least their chests moved like they were breathing. *They're alive*, she thought, *just sleeping. All you have to do now is . . .*

She had no idea.

Tempest craned her neck as Hedy returned. 'What do you have there?'

'A bucket of water,' said Hedy.

'What is it for? To dissolve a witch?'

'A witch?' On any other day, Hedy might have smiled. 'Are you talking about *The Wizard of Oz*?'

The gargoyle looked at her quizzically. 'What is that?'

– 27 –

'Oh.' Hedy gulped. She didn't want to think too hard about whether Tempest was referring to a real threat. 'No, I haven't found a witch. I *wish* fixing all this was as simple as that.'

With the gargoyle watching keenly, Hedy tipped the bucket over Spencer, Jelly and Max. The moment the water splashed them, they all stirred and snorted – the most encouraging signs Hedy had seen since she'd woken. One by one, she shook them gently by the shoulders and to her relief Spencer opened his eyes.

Jelly was the one who took longest to wake. She looked ashen and listless and it took ten minutes to get her on her feet and steady enough to walk to Grandpa John's study.

'What do we do?' Spencer asked as he studied the snow globes. 'Should we get them out?'

'You mean, crack them really gently like an egg?' said Max.

Hedy put a warning hand on Max's shoulder. 'What if that hurts them? They don't look like they're in pain right now, just sleeping.'

She bent closer to the snow globes. Lark held something in her hand, but it was hard to see what it was. 'Why would they be here in Grandpa John's study?'

Hedy mused. 'I can't imagine Grandpa John doing magic in front of Lark.'

'I bet he could feel something about to go *kapow*,' said Spencer. 'And so he came in here to get his wand to stop it. He must've been rushing since he's still got that thing on his arm.'

'Max,' said Jelly tiredly, 'go get my phone from my bag. Please.'

'Why do I have to?' Max groused automatically.

'Because I can barely walk. Hurry up. We have to call Mum, Dad, everyone. We need them to come back right now.'

A minute later, they clustered around Jelly as she dialled. First her and Max's mum, Toni. Then their dad, Vincent. Hedy and Spencer's mum and dad. Grandma Rose, Uncle Peter. All of them had been at the exhibition. But there was only endless ringing – they couldn't even reach anyone's voicemail.

Jelly frowned. 'Maybe there's something wrong with the mobile phone networks.'

'Try calling the British Museum itself,' said Hedy. 'Get them to find Mum and Dad and everyone.'

Jelly opened a browser and searched for the British Museum number. But her eyes went wide with shock.

'Oh no.' She tapped on one of the top search results, a breaking news story online.

The headline read: *British Museum Disappeared*.

Everyone craned their necks to read the article. It was very short, stating that the British Museum in central London had disappeared at around 12.35 p.m. It seemed that all visitors and staff had disappeared along with it. Authorities had been called to the site and investigations were ongoing.

'What does that mean?' Max cried. 'Is that why Mum and Dad aren't picking up?'

'I'd say so,' said Hedy.

Max looked at his sister accusingly. '*You* had a fight with Mum on the way here because you were unresponsible. Did you do this?'

'It's *irresponsible*, bozo,' Jelly said, rubbing her face. 'And as if I'd ever do this to Mum, let alone everyone else. I wouldn't even know how. Besides, if I'd found out one of Uncle John's devices could do that, I would've tried it on *you* first.'

Max let out a sharp dog bark at his sister, which he did when he couldn't think of a satisfying retort, then ran off.

'What do you think caused it?' Spencer asked.

'I bet Uncle John did it by mistake,' said Jelly. 'He tried some magic, mucked it up and it went completely—' She blew her fingers apart in an explosion.

'But things weren't right before then,' said Hedy. 'There's something wrong with magic. I don't think this is all his fault.'

'He's not perfect, Hedy. Plus he's getting old.'

'He's a grandad,' said Spencer. 'He's supposed to be old. That doesn't mean he caused this.'

Everything was round the wrong way. Daytime was night, their parents and grandparents were shrunken or unreachable, the youngsters were left in charge. Hedy felt capsized, far out at sea, and she didn't know which way to swim.

## CHAPTER 4

## A LUMP ON A RUMP

Max came skidding back into the kitchen. 'Come and look,' he panted.

On the lounge floor, three small lumps about the size of billiard balls were frozen in place in the wooden floorboards.

'Oh no, not the Woodspies,' sighed Hedy.

Their playful little friends who travelled through anything and everything wooden didn't budge when Hedy nudged them with a knuckle. They'd apparently been in the middle of some mischief – the straps of Lark's bag had been sucked into the wooden floor.

Spencer knelt down to gingerly pick through Lark's belongings. 'Do you think we should call someone for her?'

'Like who?' said Jelly.

'Her family or the hospital? What hospital does she work for anyway?'

But they couldn't find anything like an identification card or pass for wherever Lark worked.

'And what would we say to them?' Jelly said. 'We couldn't tell them what's *actually* happened to her.'

As they stared morosely at the mess the Woodspies had made, there was a commotion above. Stomping, a loud cry and a heavy crash to the floor.

*What else could go wrong?* Hedy thought as they raced up the stairs.

The ruckus was coming from the Green Room – the room with the dark-green door next to their bedroom when they stayed. On an ordinary day, the Green Room was remarkable enough with its large collection jars, the metal wings, and of course their friends Doug the bear rug and Stan the stuffed stag's head. Flinging open the door, Hedy and the others were greeted with the strangest sight of their lives: a brown bear with the long spindly legs of a deer was struggling to its feet, with an antlered stag's head atop the bear's round bottom.

'Well, something's done it now, Stan,' rumbled Doug with a backwards look. 'You're a lump on my rump! How in the world do you walk on these twigs? I feel like they could barely hold up a rabbit.'

'A deer's legs are made to hold up the muscle of a powerful stag and his resplendent antlers,' retorted Stan, 'not the mass of an overindulgent beast such as yourself.'

'It's not overindulgence, it's nature,' Doug huffed. 'You try hibernating without extra fat to keep you going.'

In spite of all that was wrong at Hoarder Hill, knowing that Doug and Stan were not stuck in an enchanted sleep felt like a win to Hedy. The habitual squabbling of the bear and the stag lifted all their spirits.

Doug turned to face Spencer and the others. 'Cubs, what's been happening? One moment we're talking about acorns and the next we wake up on the floor, it's dark outside and we're in this right jumble. We need the Master to unscramble us.'

'Quite right,' said Stan, swivelling their joint body

around to face them. 'I know the Master has his rule against the doing of magic but there will be no peace in this abode until Doug and I are separated once more. How one is supposed to think with a bear's posterior right under one's nose, I cannot tell you.'

'Grandpa John can't,' Spencer said bluntly. 'We're the only ones left.'

'Only ones left?' Stan asked. 'What do you mean? Where have they gone?'

When the animals had been told what had happened, they asked to see the snow globes. Doug even poked out his tongue to taste the glass.

'Tastes like magic,' growled Doug, 'but it doesn't taste like the house. It's magic newly arrived. Hasn't lived here and taken on the flavour of Hoarder Hill.'

Stan swung their body away with a skip. 'Stop licking things, you reckless blockhead, or we'll be stuck in one of those glass baubles before you can say . . . well, before you can say, "Stop licking that!"'

'I've licked worse,' said Doug. 'Cubs, is there *anyone* left to help?'

Hedy stared at the ceiling, thinking. Two names came to her. 'Mrs Vilums. And Mrs Pal.'

Spencer nodded. 'I'll try calling Mrs Pal now.' She

was the only maker they knew, and even more know-ledgeable about magical devices than Grandpa John because she traded them through her shop, the Palisade. Mrs Vilums had been the housekeeper at Hoarder Hill, and now lived with her sisters here in Marberry's Rest. But there was more to her than that.

'I'll see if Mrs Vilums is home,' said Hedy.

Jelly hiked a thumb at the blue-black sky visible through the window. 'Will you be able to get out? We don't know what that darkness does.'

'Well, I have to try.'

As they walked Hedy to the front gate, Spencer asked, 'Should one of us come with you?'

'Guard the house,' Hedy said firmly. 'And especially Grandpa John and Lark. I won't be long.'

Despite her matter-of-fact tone, her hand quivered as she reached for the gate of the front garden, where the dome of night ended. There was the slightest feeling of resistance as she slowly pulled the gate open and eased herself out of the darkness and on to the footpath.

The sun seemed so bright out here. Hedy squinted back over her shoulder, finding that the house looked completely normal. There was no suggestion of the dark dome overhead, and yet neither could she see

Spencer, Jelly or Max who were just a few metres away on the garden path. She retreated through the gate, relieved she could get back in, and they reappeared.

'The dome must be a sort of disguise for the house,' she told them. 'From out there Hoarder Hill looks completely normal, no darkness. But I can't see any of you.'

'Can I try?' Spencer asked.

'Don't pop in and out too much,' said Jelly. 'Greedy Grutz might get suspicious if you appear and disappear over and over again.'

'Go and call Mrs Pal,' said Hedy. 'I'll be back soon. Hopefully with Mrs V.'

Running fast, it took Hedy only a few minutes to reach Mrs Vilums's house, closer to the heart of the village. *Thank goodness they're not in Namibia or some faraway place right now*, she thought. When the children had first met her, Mrs Vilums had secretly turned into a garden statue every night. After being locked in stone for years, she and her sisters loved to travel far and wide, making up for lost time.

She burst through their garden gate and hammered the knocker on the front door. All was quiet. Too quiet. Her racing pulse was loud in her ears. Hedy knocked again. It never usually took this long for one of them to answer the door.

Down the side of the cottage, the sisters grew purple columbines and daisies. Hedy muttered an apology under her breath for shoving the flowers aside roughly as she tried to peer through the windows. Nothing seemed amiss in the first room, or the second. It was the view through the third window that made her freeze.

Hedy stared and stared, and after a while, realized she was focusing on unimportant details. Plates of half-eaten pitta bread and salad before the three women. They must have been having lunch. It was as though her brain wanted to skate over the real blow: Mrs Vilums, Maja and Ewa sitting around their table, transformed into motionless black stone statues.

Whatever had happened earlier – the explosion of magical force that had shaken Hoarder Hill and had caused the British Museum and everyone in it to disappear – had washed through here too.

As Hedy retraced her steps to Hoarder Hill, her thoughts in a whirl, she found a tall, hunched figure pushing at the gate. Mr Grutz.

'Can I help you?' she asked coldly.

Mr Grutz started. 'I need to speak with your grandfather.'

'He's resting,' said Hedy. She wasn't exactly lying.

'It's important. Urgent.'

'I can give him a message when he wakes up.'

Mr Grutz looked at the house again. 'Is everything all right in there?'

*The crusty old snoop knows something*, Hedy thought. The way his eyes ran over the place was too probing. She didn't trust him. 'Everything's fine, thank you.' She could see from his expression that he didn't trust her either.

As she pushed the gate open, smugly aware that Mr Grutz had been expecting her to struggle with it as he had, he held out an envelope. 'Give this to him.'

Not even a 'please', which annoyed Hedy further. She took the envelope with a frosty nod. When he had gone back to his own house, she finally closed the garden gate and carefully opened the envelope. The note inside it read: *I know where to find the ancient one.*

'What ancient one?' Hedy mumbled to herself. She shoved the note into her pocket, wishing she *could* give it to Grandpa John and pester him about it.

Spencer answered the front door. His face fell when he saw Hedy was alone. 'Wasn't Mrs Vilums home?'

'She and Maja and Ewa have turned back to stone,' said Hedy heavily. 'Did you get through to Mrs Pal?'

Spencer shook his head. 'No answer. Not even the answering machine.'

The helplessness on Spencer's face was exactly what Hedy was feeling. 'Where are Jelly and Max?'

'The attic. Jelly has a theory.'

'Uh-oh.'

The floor beneath the attic was puddling with sand. A steady stream of it was falling down the stairs.

'Where is this coming from?' Hedy asked.

'Come and see,' said Spencer.

It was flowing out of Grandpa John's secret room in the attic. The door was open and beyond it was Grandpa John's large magic box, the Kaleidos. But the Kaleidos was not lying immobile as it should have been. Its glimmering cubes were whirling of their own accord in a funnel as tall as Hedy herself, spinning slowly, like a cement mixer. The sand spilt from within its depths.

'I don't think we should hang around *this*,' said Hedy.

'No dilly-dallying,' agreed Jelly. 'But we do need Uncle John's notebook. Hear me out. It's got to be connected – his trip and magic going wrong and all of *this*.' She waved her arm around the whole house. 'The notebook and Sir Roland's sword must be part of the puzzle. Hedy, you saw how twitchy Uncle John got when you put two and two together before, which basically proves we need them to put things right.'

'But magic going wrong feels too big and mysterious for us to figure out,' said Spencer.

Jelly scratched her head. 'If we're the only ones left to fix what's happening, we're so doomed,' she said. 'Maybe we just need to get the gauntlet and the notebook to the bigwigs. Bigger wigs than even Uncle John.'

Hedy realized who Jelly meant. The group of senior magicians who governed the magical community would solve this and make it right. She nodded. 'We need the Sleight.'

## CHAPTER 5

## THE GAUNTLET

T he mysterious explosion earlier had knocked Sir Roland flat on to the floor of the attic. He wasn't disobedient any more but rather entirely unresponsive. His sword, however, was still stuck upright in the floor, pinning the notebook. Jealously clenching the sword hilt was his steel gauntlet, detached from the rest of the armour.

Hedy stooped to peek inside the notebook but couldn't see much – the notebook was too small and its leather-bound cover was too rigid to lift up while speared. But the sword may as well have been embedded in some kind of rock. Hedy gripped its cross-guard and tried to lift it free, but she couldn't make it move by even a hair.

'What if I try to put my hand inside the gauntlet?' said Spencer.

'Sir Roland might get cranky and go on the attack if we use him like a costume,' said Hedy. 'Don't forget how he came at us that first time.'

Although Sir Roland was at Grandpa John's command, he'd once tried to slice them up, like a robot stuck in 'exterminate' mode.

'Max, get back over here,' Jelly called out to her brother who was tiptoeing towards the whirling Kaleidos. 'The last thing we need is you getting sucked into the magic box.'

'Sand is coming *out*,' said Max, 'not being sucked in.'

'Knowing you, you'll accidentally kick some reverse gear and be the first thing it gobbles up.'

Spencer tried a variation of the words Grandpa John had used to control the armour, when it had attacked them years ago. '*Rise up. I am thy master and my purpose is pure.*' But the armour ignored him.

Max skipped over. 'Did you try this, Spence?' Before anyone could stop him, he slipped his hand into the large, empty gauntlet.

Instantly the overlapping steel plates of the gauntlet squeezed in tightly over Max's small hand and wrist. Max yelped and tried to pull his hand free, but he was trapped inside. At the jerk of his hand, however, the sword was yanked out of the wood. Before their eyes, the long shiny blade swiftly shrank down into the hilt, the cross-guard disappeared and the hilt itself telescoped inwards. Grandpa John's notebook fell to the floor with a thump and Max, hand still encased, was left holding only the pommel of the sword.

'I did it! I'm like King Arthur!' crowed Max, pointing to the freed notebook. His face fell, however, as he tried and failed to wiggle his hand out of the gauntlet.

'Yeah, I think you've done it, all right,' said Hedy sarcastically. Examining the pommel, she saw that it was now decorated with an emblem of a sun.

Jelly took hold of the gauntlet and tried to tug it off her brother's hand, but had no more luck than Max. 'This place is turning into Disaster Central! Every train from bad luck to catastrophe is coming through. If we don't get Max out of this thing, his hand might fall off. I mean, *best* case scenario it's going to turn all white and pruney inside and start smelling like a rotting fish burger.'

'Don't say that,' said Spencer, making a retching noise. 'You'll turn me off fish burgers.'

Hedy paged through Grandpa John's notebook. Curiously, the right-hand pages were all blank. His writing appeared only on the left-hand pages. But there was a problem. 'I can't read this. I doubt any of us can. It's written in a whole heap of different languages.'

'What do we do?' Spencer asked. 'Use an online translator?'

'It would take ages, but I guess that's the only option we have. Look at this one sentence – Spanish, Mandarin, German, Arabic and . . . I don't even know what language *that* is.'

They were interrupted by Doug and Stan calling out their names. Wary of the sand leaking endlessly out of the Kaleidos, Hedy motioned for them all to head from the attic down to the second floor.

'What is it, Stoug?' Jelly asked.

Doug narrowed his eyes. 'What's a "stoug"?'

'That's your new combined nickname, your portmanteau. Stan and Doug together.'

'If that is what you are proposing to call us from now on,' said Stan, 'you had better not expect an answer.' He primly changed the subject. 'Our room was rattling like a china cabinet in an earthquake. We had no idea the Master had stored so many things in there that were enchanted. After years of lying dormant, they have woken up.'

'Topsy-turvy is all turvy-topsy and that means trouble,' growled Doug. 'I don't think it's safe to stay here. Speaking of trouble—' He broke off, ears twitching. 'Do you hear that?'

They could hardly miss it: a discordant run of piano notes punctuated by angry chords. It was coming from the Yellow Room, the one with the yellow door.

When they entered the Yellow Room, Simon the ghost pianist turned on his stool and cried, 'Harmony, melody, tunefulness! It is all gone!' He snatched up the sheaf of papers on top of the piano and shook them. They captured his last composition before he died, a piano concerto. 'The notes are changed and I am nothing!'

Simon's concerto was not the only thing that seemed off. The rug slapped against the side of the piano as though trying to free itself, making Hedy wonder if all this time it had been an out-of-action flying carpet. On top of the piano, the bust of Lord

Wellington had closed his eyes and was murmuring to himself.

'Hush your wailing, Simon. You are not the only one suffering,' said Stan as he and Doug jostled into the room.

At the sight of the two animals stuck together, Simon dropped his composition, appalled, and gabbled something in his native French that none of them could understand. 'Who has done this to us?' he said at last when the shock wore off.

They told Simon all they knew, making him tut and *tsk*. 'And it has set off the Master's protective defence?'

'Defence?' asked Hedy.

Simon wafted to the window and pointed a long, transparent finger at the night-looking sky beyond the glass. 'The Obscurity, it is called. The darkness that conceals the house. From outside the Obscurity, nothing improper can be seen. It is a mask. My guess is that Monsieur Sang has had it waiting in the wings for years. And when the house was attacked, it was set off.'

'Like a trap?' asked Max, shuffling closer to Doug and Stan. 'Is the bad guy trapped here in the house?'

Doug nudged Max with his wet nose. 'Easy, cub. I can't smell any strangers here.'

'I do not believe the Obscurity stops things getting out,' Simon said, 'so it is not a trap in that sense. Its purpose is more likely to give Monsieur Sang time. Time to restore the right way of things.'

'Except that Grandpa John can't do any restoring,' said Spencer. He turned to Hedy. 'The Sleight will come to help, won't they?'

Hedy nodded, wishing she felt more certain about it.

'How will my concerto live on if this turmoil is not stopped?' Simon murmured, slumping by the window. 'Its notes and rests are scrambled like an omelette made with eggs gone foul.' Although he seemed ready to brood upon his own misery for some time, something outside caught his eye. He stuck his head through the window to get a better look. 'Is this fellow the one you have been waiting for? Perhaps help has arrived already!'

The children darted to the window to look, and to their alarm saw Mr Grutz trying to wrench at the gate.

'He's not help,' said Hedy. 'He's the nosy neighbour who tries to spy on Grandpa John.'

'Why does he want to get in so badly?' asked Max.

Jelly snapped her fingers. 'Maybe Greedy Grutz is a

rogue magician. And he's the one who made all this happen!'

Hedy had to admit that Jelly's theory made sense of Mr Grutz's persistent prying. Magicians were a secretive and highly competitive lot. They had heard of magicians trying to steal secrets before.

'But he doesn't look anything like a magician,' Max sneered.

'You can't judge a book by its cover,' said Hedy.

Max looked dubious. 'I *always* pick a book cos of its cover.'

'What I meant was, hardly any of the other magicians we've met look magician-y.'

'If he is a magician, he's not as good as Grandpa John,' said Spencer. 'Hedy could get back in but the gate hasn't moved for Greedy Grutz. The Obscurity must be keeping it shut against anyone but family.'

A minute later, they spied Mr Grutz prowling through his front garden by the fence bordering Hoarder Hill.

'He's trying to jump over the fence!' said Jelly.

The hedges growing along their side, however, seemed to have other ideas. They swished back and forth as though shooing him away, and he couldn't seem to get a grip on the fence to climb over. He stalked back into his house.

'He's given up, and good riddance to him,' sniffed Stan.

All too soon, however, Mr Grutz hurried back out, with a stubborn set to his shoulders and something in his hand. It looked like a pickaxe.

A few moments later, a sliver of late afternoon light pierced the Obscurity for the first time since they'd woken. Whatever Mr Grutz's tool was, he had used it to make a crack in the dome of night over Hoarder Hill.

## CHAPTER 6

## THE OTHER SIDE OF THE HILL

The afternoon sun shone for only a few seconds before the crack closed up again. Less than a minute later, however, another crack appeared, bigger than the first. The dome of the Obscurity pulsed, darkening for a moment, and closed the gap once more, but that didn't deter Mr Grutz. Each time he smashed his pickaxe into the darkness, it chipped open a bigger hole.

'Sooner or later he's going to get through,' Spencer gulped. 'Then what do we do?'

At Mr Grutz's next blow, the darkness over the

house seemed to shiver. This time, the daylight sneaking through lasted longer than any before it.

*Crash!* Hedy spun around as the room shook, to find that Doug and Stan had fallen to the floor in a heap of fur and antlers.

'Oh dear, I fear whatever is happening is not at all good for us,' said Stan, looking disorientated. 'Doug, do you feel well? For I do not!'

Doug's only answer was a long growl with a touch of menace Hedy had never heard from the bear in all the time they had known him.

On the floor the small rug had ceased its flapping against the side of the piano, but threads that had worked loose were pulling this way and that, undoing the weave of the rug as though it was trying to unmake itself.

'*Mon dieu!*' Simon gazed at his ghostly hands which seemed to have faded, leaving him more transparent than before. He rushed towards his beloved grand piano, but when he pressed his fingers to the keys they passed right through. 'I cannot play! Whatever is happening is making me less than I was!'

There was another shudder in the Obscurity that prompted a second growl from Doug, louder than the last.

'Hard pounding this, gentlemen; let's see who will pound longest,' said an unfamiliar voice. It was the bust of Lord Wellington on top of the piano. Hedy was taken aback, for the bust had never addressed them before. 'Up, guards, and at them!' he added.

'Ignore the statuette,' Simon scowled. 'He offers no meaning. He only spouts historical quotations by the Duke of Wellington.' Under his breath, the ghost added, 'May the fiend suffer eternal indigestion for his defeat over the French at Waterloo.'

Hedy, however, had a sense that the bust really was trying to tell them something. 'At them? At who?'

But at that moment, Jelly groaned. Grey-faced, she swayed into Hedy's side. 'I don't feel so great. Actually, I'm feeling really gross.' Even her hair, which normally seemed to have a life of its own, appeared to have wilted.

'Are you going to throw up?' Max asked. He hopped nervously from foot to foot, a little too close to Doug's nose and the bear snapped, making Max yelp in fright.

'Douglas! Stop that at once!' gasped Stan. 'Children, we must get away from the house. Whatever is happening is a danger to us. It's making Doug turn very strange. The last thing we need is a baleful bear on my backside.'

From other reaches of the house, there were faint noises of things moving that had not moved in decades. Even the books on top of the piano were trembling in a worrisome way.

Hedy couldn't get her thoughts straight; too much was happening at once. 'Get away to where?'

'The Sleight,' said Spencer. 'If we head towards them, it'll be faster than waiting for them to come to us.'

'But what about the house?' asked Hedy, feeling torn. 'Shouldn't we stay here and protect it from Mr Grutz?'

The bust of Lord Wellington rolled to its side to look Hedy earnestly in the eye. 'All the business of war, and indeed all the business of life, is to endeavour to find out what you don't know by what you do; that's what I called "guessing what was at the other side of the hill".'

*Endeavour to find out what you don't know.* Lord Wellington's words pierced the pandemonium in Hedy's mind. What was at the other side of Hoarder Hill?

Hedy began barking orders like a field marshal herself: pack the most important things, gather in the kitchen, head to the statue graveyard.

Stan heaved his and Doug's body up on to their hooves and headed for the door, talking in a soothing tone. 'Come now, Doug, we are going on another adventure with the youngsters, and we will get you back to your old self faster than a brown hare. No, you can stop that growling, you have nothing to be irritable about. *I'm* the one having to make our legs go backwards down the stairs and it is extremely difficult, let me tell you.'

Jelly was still unsteady, and had to be helped downstairs by Max.

Max waggled the gauntlet on his hand. 'What do I do about this?'

'Like it or not, it has to come with us,' said Hedy. She turned to Spencer. 'Get some food and water. And grab that big torch from under the sink. I'll get the snow globes.'

'Fine, Captain Bossy-Pants,' Spencer grumbled.

'Well, be practical and I won't have to boss you,' Hedy sighed, shooing him towards the door.

They found the doorway blocked by Simon. 'Children, I beg of you, take me too. I fear that if I stay, I shall dwindle to nothing.'

'We can't take a piano!' exclaimed Spencer.

'You do not need to take the piano,' said Simon. 'Put my composition inside the piano stool, and take the stool with you. The stool is my anchor, you see. And the composition my soul.'

'I'm sorry, Simon,' said Hedy, 'but it will slow us down. What if we have to run?'

The ghost pianist bit his lip. 'Oblivion awaits me. Three centuries I have had to prepare and still I cannot welcome it.'

Hedy felt terrible. Simon had saved their family from Albert Nobody once. How could they sentence him to oblivion?

Spencer nudged her. 'We could at least get Simon away from the house. And if we can't run with the stool any more then we find a safe place to hide it until it's OK for us to come back.'

'Let's do that,' Hedy agreed. 'Simon, back up while I take your stool downstairs. And you'll have to keep your distance so we don't touch you by accident. We'll be underground soon, so we can't risk anyone catching your death chill.' They all knew they could not touch a ghost – or the cold of the grave would enter their own bones.

*

A short time later, they had some supplies and the snow globes had been padded with a towel and carefully packed into Hedy's bag. They locked all the house doors and began making their way by torchlight towards the statue graveyard at the bottom of the garden.

As they passed the garage, Spencer broke away, saying, 'One second. I have an idea. A *practical* one,' he added at Hedy's exasperated look.

He returned with a long, leathery cord – Hedy's troll's whisker from their last adventure. 'For Simon's piano stool.'

Hedy helped him flip Simon's piano stool over the back of Doug and Stan and sling the leathery whisker around them a few times. Something else that Spencer had grabbed from the garage caught her eye.

'How is the skyskepnur practical?' she couldn't help saying.

Spencer shrugged. 'I don't want it wasting away here and its magic to go wrong.'

Something swooped overhead, making their hair swish.

'What are you all doing?' asked Tempest. 'The Greedy Grutz is trying to breach the defence. He is on the other side of the house. Come, I will show you.'

'We know,' said Hedy.

'But you're going in the wrong direction,' said Tempest as though she was thick-headed. 'You must meet him there and attack! Or is your plan to strike him with a long-range missile from this side of the house?' She peered at Spencer tying the piano stool to Doug and Stan. 'Is this bear-stag-stool contraption your engine of war? I worry that you will not clear the roof with it.'

'We're kids,' Hedy said. 'We don't have an engine of war and we're not attacking him. We're leaving to find help.'

Tempest began to argue, calling them cowards, shirkers, deserters and a host of other choice names.

'Hey!' Jelly suddenly interjected, silencing the gargoyle. She glanced fearfully at the house. 'I think we'd better get further away. I feel like something's going to burst.'

'Do you need to go to the toilet?' Max asked, confused.

'Not me, silly. Something in the house.'

Whatever she felt, Doug also seemed to sense. He let out a low moan and began to trot towards the bottom of the garden. At Jelly's urging, they all followed him, even Tempest.

They'd made it through the archway of climbing roses when an unearthly sound pierced the false night. It began as a deep hum and ascended to a shriek, before abruptly ceasing. There was a heavy beat of silence and then the windows of Hoarder Hill shattered, sand exploding out.

'The Kaleidos!' gasped Spencer.

Hedy shuddered to think what it looked like inside the house. Throwing an arm around Jelly to help her cousin run, she cried, 'Get to the Slip!'

They dashed onwards, stumbling and tripping as Max's torchlight zigzagged from side to side. Reaching the walled-off area where Grandpa John's large stone statues were kept, Spencer shouted, 'Copenhagen! We need help!'

They all covered their ears as the enormous Chinese lion statue roared, making their bones quiver. Hedy had once read that a lion's roar could be heard nearly ten kilometres away, and she was sure this stone lion's sound was just as powerful as that. It was why Grandpa John seldom let them open this gateway: he didn't want to have to explain loud and peculiar noises coming from the garden to the neighbours – or, indeed, the whole of Marberry's Rest. She prayed that the Obscurity kept the noise from Mr Grutz.

'I'm half deaf,' complained Max as he let his hands drop. 'The gauntlet just made the roar louder!'

A trace of a crack appeared in the centre of the stone lion's head and then, as though being unzipped, it split wide open to reveal a tunnel leading downwards. They slid into it and the opening closed behind them.

In the middle of the earthen tunnel was a metal bollard, no taller than Hedy's waist and with a top shaped like a horse's head. This was Copenhagen, sentry of the slipway leading away from Hoarder Hill, and – as he had proudly told them on the day he was installed – namesake of the Duke of Wellington's horse. *It's a real Duke of Wellington-themed day*, Hedy mused.

'Whatever is going on?' Copenhagen asked. 'Everyone from here to the white cliffs of Dover will hear you! Your grandfather will be crosser than a mule on Monday.'

'No, he won't,' Hedy panted. 'Some sort of magic has trapped him and put him to sleep. And the rest of our family has disappeared.'

'Plus, the house just exploded with sand,' added Jelly, 'and the neighbour is trying to break through Uncle John's magical force field that's covering the house. Also,' she pointed at Doug and Stan, 'it made a Stoug.'

'We need help,' said Spencer, peering along the slipway. 'We need the Sleight.'

Copenhagen's ears pricked in alarm. 'This is very troubling news indeed. I cannot seem to reach Bucephalus right now.'

Bucephalus was a bollard just like Copenhagen, gatekeeper to the Sleight's headquarters in Edinburgh.

'Are you saying Bucephalus is out of action?' Hedy asked, stomach sinking. 'And does that mean the Sleight is out of action too?'

Copenhagen whinnied. 'What will you do? Will you wait here?'

'No,' said Hedy, 'we won't find any answers sitting here. We need the Sleight to figure this out and fix it. We can find our way to the Edinburgh vaults well enough.'

Stan gazed at Copenhagen with his most imperious look. 'You must not let anyone into the Slip behind us.'

The sentry tossed his head and mane. 'Not a soul.'

## CHAPTER 7

## FOOTSTEPS IN THE DARK

Edinburgh was a solid day's drive by car. But by walking the magical tunnel known as the Slip, they would be able to cover the distance to the Sleight's headquarters in a little less than two hours. They could hardly get lost, because the only slipway detour from this tunnel was to Mrs Pal's shop, the Palisade. As far as Hedy was aware, Grandpa John had never used the Slip to travel anywhere else.

The further they went from Hoarder Hill, the better Jelly seemed to feel. Even in torchlight, they could tell that the colour was returning to her face, and after sucking on a few fruit pastilles she was able to walk without help.

Before they had reached the slipway opening for the Palisade, a noise echoed through the tunnel – the sound of footsteps ahead of them in the dark. Doug, who still seemed unable to speak as he normally did, began to rumble deep in his chest and his head strained forwards.

'Douglas, you must not go charging into dangers unknown,' said Stan, trying to control the belligerent bear. 'Don't forget you have a deer on your rear!'

All of them stopped walking and drew closer to Doug and Stan for protection; except for Tempest, who reared up on her claws and flared her wings, prepared to attack whoever was out there.

Beside Spencer, Max gasped. There was a cold metallic *shhhhk* sound as the orb in Sir Roland's gauntlet turned itself inside out, reversing its transformation in the attic. In an instant, Max was gripping a hilt and shining blade again, so heavy that he needed to use both hands to lift the sword point from the ground.

Hedy shone the torch ahead. The footsteps slowed but they didn't stop until a tall shape emerged from the dark of the Slip. It was a lean man dressed entirely in black, holding up a lantern that illuminated his hawk-ish nose.

'Bess!' Hedy exclaimed. 'You scared us!'

'Trust me, your troop is much more fearsome than I am,' Bess replied.

Spencer squinted. 'You're making fun of us,' he accused.

It could be very hard to tell when the treasure hunter was mocking people and, in Hedy's opinion, usually safest to assume that he was.

'Am I?' Bess joined them and slung his pack to the ground. 'A gargoyle, a brown bear, a fourteen-point stag and four seasoned adventurers? I'd put my money on you any day. Plus, a moment ago, there was a big sword looking like it wanted to get jabby in my direction.' He tilted his head at Max. 'What did you do with it?'

Max shrugged, bewildered. The sword was gone and only the orb of the pommel was left in Sir Roland's gauntlet. 'It disappeared again after Hedy called your name.'

Bess studied their group, brow knitted. 'I'm truly glad to see you all. But given John is not with you . . .'

'Well, he is, sort of,' said Hedy. She unzipped her

backpack to show Bess the snow globes.

'Stars,' Bess muttered. He held Grandpa John's snow globe close to his lantern. 'I was hoping that he'd been spared.'

'Do you mean other magicians are trapped in snow globes too?'

'Not snow globes,' said Bess grimly, 'but other confinements, just as bad. I'll show you.'

He rummaged in his bag and took out a gadget that looked like something an optician might have used generations ago: a hefty lens rimmed with dials, held up by a worn wooden handle. Bess brought the lens to his eye and fiddled with the dials. A moment later, a vivid image sprang up around them.

Hedy felt her perspective abruptly change. She was taller, adult-height, the floor at least half a metre further away than she was used to. Bess wasn't merely projecting what he had seen, he had taken them inside his memory.

Hedy felt like she was in the Sleight's grand meeting room, the Peacock Chamber, and in her palm was a large sapphire ring. The ring was familiar; it belonged to Candice Harding, the leader of the Sleight. Lifting the ring closer, Hedy could see a face inside the deep blue gem – Candice herself, trapped.

Like a kaleidoscope turning, the memory engulfing her broke and twisted into something different. This time, her hands (man-sized, she noted) were holding open a parchment scroll. It was a sketch of Flora Maymon, another friend of theirs in the Sleight. When the sleeping, sketched figure moved, Hedy realized that Flora hadn't only been miniaturized but trapped as a picture in the scroll.

At the next turn of the image surrounding them, she was picking up an hourglass from the floor. As she stood it upright, the sand trickled into the bottom chamber, revealing that the top of the hourglass held the unconscious form of their distant cousin, Ewan Tsang, shrunken to the size of a jelly baby.

When the image next broke apart and twisted, it disappeared altogether. Hedy looked around. The others were all blinking with the astonishment she felt, even Simon.

'You've seen what I've seen now,' said Bess, folding down his lens device. 'As far as I can tell, every magician in the British Isles has been subdued.'

*Every magician subdued?* Hedy swayed and squeezed Grandpa John's snow globe, feeling hopeless.

Her plan – find the Sleight, have them fix things – had already fallen apart. 'Our parents, our grandmother and Uncle Peter have all disappeared too,' she said numbly. The fact that they were gone was something she couldn't face head-on yet. They weren't magicians; they shouldn't have been swept up in this.

They filled Bess in on everything – their family vanishing with the British Museum, the house and the Obscurity, and Mr Grutz. Bess's usually impassive expression grew very bleak.

He pointed at the other snow globe in Hedy's bag. 'Who's that?'

'That's Lark,' said Spencer. 'Grandpa's carer.'

'Why is she trapped too? Is she a magician?'

Spencer shook his head. 'I think she was wrong time, wrong place.'

'OK, Bess, time to spill,' said Jelly, sounding much sprightlier than before. 'What's going on? Why were you going on your sneaky trip with Uncle John? We know it has something to do with magic going wrong.'

Bess stared up at the tunnel ceiling for a long while. Finally, he said, 'You're right. Magic is . . . unspooling. Not working properly. The Sleight first noticed it weakening a few months ago, but lately it's had ripples, almost convulsions. When these ripples happen, magic goes haywire. John was going on a trip to try to put things right. I was commissioned to be his bodyguard, and nursemaid if his health took a turn.'

'Where were you going?' Hedy asked. 'What did you have to do?'

'France,' said Bess. 'I had to get John and a special sword of his to Paris. In Paris, he had to locate *something* and then we had to take that something to the Spellbound Tree.' He held up a hand. 'And before you ask, I don't truly know what the Spellbound Tree is or where it is. Need-to-know basis only. All I know is that it's somehow connected to magic starting to fail.'

*The Spellbound Tree.* Hedy felt a flutter at the name, foreboding and thrill intertwined.

'Do you think Mr Grutz has something to do with it?'

Bess waggled a hand uncertainly. 'He's no magician. He's bog – the Sleight looked into him when he moved in next to your grandparents. But there are plenty of bogs who'd be happy to see magic fail entirely. The fact he had a tool that could break the Obscurity over your grandparents' house? I don't like the sound of that.'

The bloodhound sense in Hedy had pricked up its ears at Bess's words. For the first time all this terribly long day, she had the tiniest flicker of hope that they had something to work with. 'Did you say "special sword"?' She pointed at Max's gauntlet. 'It must be this jack-in-the-box one that Max has managed to get stuck on to his hand. Grandpa John was trying to get Sir Roland to hand it over before you arrived.'

'Show us the sword again, Max,' said Jelly.

Max lifted the gauntlet and shook it but the blade would not appear. 'I don't know how.'

'You must know,' said Jelly impatiently. 'You had it out before, when Bess was sneaking up on us.'

'I didn't do anything except almost pee my pants, I was so scared,' Max said.

'Perhaps,' said Bess, 'the sword is in hiding and only appears when threatened. A reaction to danger.'

Without warning, Tempest shrieked and leapt towards Max, her wings and claws outstretched. Everyone cried out, and there was a roar as Doug and Stan launched at the gargoyle, batting her down with a long leg and then pinning her to the tunnel floor by a bear's muzzle.

'It was a ruse!' Tempest choked out. 'Look! I made

the sword appear!'

It was true. In the hubbub, the pommel had transformed and wide-eyed Max was once again holding Sir Roland's broadsword.

Bess began to laugh in disbelief. 'Of course you have it, Max. I never knew a family to get itself into trouble like you lot. Now, if only we knew what to do with it.'

While Stan berated Tempest for scaring the wits out of everyone, Hedy searched her backpack. Down the bottom was Grandpa John's notebook from the attic, the one that none of them had been able to read. She held it out to Bess. 'Do you know how to read this?'

The treasure hunter quickly ran his eyes over a few pages, but his expression told Hedy the script was as incomprehensible to him as it had been to them. 'Your grandfather has used a Rosetta Jumbler on this,' he said. 'I guess you'd describe it as a magical coding device. What's written here will be in a thousand different languages. But look at this.' He pointed to the word *Baum*. 'German for "tree". I think you've found his notes on what he had to do to get to the Spellbound Tree.'

'How do we decode the rest of the notebook?' said Hedy.

'A Rosetta Jumbler looks like a glass pyramid less than a hand span high,' said Bess. 'Ever seen that at Hoarder Hill?'

'I once saw something like that on Grandpa John's desk,' said Spencer, 'I thought it was a paperweight.'

'But the house isn't safe to go back to,' said Hedy.

Bess thought for a while. 'Paris is a big city. I might know someone who could help with a Rosetta Jumbler there.'

'Paris!' exclaimed Simon, clapping his ghostly hands. 'Why, I have not been there since I was alive!'

## CHAPTER 8

## PARIS

They continued north towards Edinburgh, but as they neared the vaults Bess diverted from the main path and led them to an unfamiliar chamber. It had an ancient but stout-looking door and nailed into the door was a sign that read, '*La France*'.

Bess had to wrestle with the door to open it. 'This way.'

Jelly wrinkled her nose at the fusty air that wafted through. 'Phew. Doesn't exactly smell like croissants down here, does it.'

'I'd really love a croissant right now,' Spencer sighed.

'Keep walking and we might be able to do something about that,' said Bess.

He was answered by a low growl reverberating in the tunnel.

'Now, now, none of that, Doug,' chided Stan, who had to twist his head awkwardly to fit his antlers through the doorway.

'It wasn't Doug,' said Spencer. 'That was my empty stomach.'

A few minutes into the new tunnel, Hedy picked up the sound of muffled voices through the walls. 'I can hear people talking,' she whispered.

'Probably just tourists,' explained Bess.

Hedy looked at him sceptically. 'This late at night? Down here?'

Bess shrugged. 'Ghost tours in the vaults are very popular. Not that they get to see much.'

A minute later, the muffled voices became shrieks and shouts. They halted in their tracks, scanning the slipway walls for signs of danger. The reason for the screaming became clear, however, when Simon floated through the brickwork, chuckling to himself.

'What did you do?' Tempest demanded.

'Monsieur Bess said the visitors do not get to see

much,' said Simon innocently. 'These Scottish ghosts are so very dull and sluggish. I simply gave the people something to make their tour . . . memorable.' He sighed. 'Unfortunately, I do not think my Scottish accent was very good.'

Bess waved everyone forwards wearily. But after a few minutes, even he began to see the funny side and, for the first time in a century, the slipway to Paris echoed with laughter.

They walked for nearly two more hours. It was past their bedtime now, and the chatter died away, replaced by yawns and long stretches of tired silence.

'Max, pick up your feet,' said Jelly. 'It's so annoying when you drag them along like that.'

'You're not the one carrying a metal glove that weighs a tonne,' Max retorted.

'Mum will freak out about your shoes getting holes.'

'Good,' he said. 'At least that'll mean she's back with us and OK.'

Hedy squeezed Max on the shoulder and Jelly swallowed whatever she had been about to say. He was the youngest of all of them and considering everything that had happened, he'd been pretty resilient. After a moment Jelly reached for her brother's gauntleted hand and held it to take some of the weight for him.

When the slipway began to slope upwards, Bess told them with relief that they were near the Paris exit. Buoyed, they all picked up the pace.

Before they reached their exit, however, Jelly stumbled to a stop and thrust a hand against the slipway wall. 'I don't feel so great. Everything's spinning.'

'The ripple in magic that Bess spoke of,' said Tempest. The gargoyle flexed her neck uncomfortably. 'I believe it's happening again.'

Hedy reached into her backpack for the snow globes, stomach tensing at the thought that something else was about to go wrong with Grandpa John and poor Lark.

There was a curious noise over her shoulder. Doug's head hung very low to the ground and he was growling, while Stan let out a strange long grunt. The stag's antlers strained in the opposite direction, back towards the way from which they had come, and then Stan somehow popped out and backwards from Doug, the long deer legs going with him. Off balance, Doug face-planted into the rock, momentarily bewildered by the clawed paws that had reappeared beneath his heavy, all-bear body. They had separated, and with full bodies too. Simon's piano stool crashed to the ground, prompting the ghost to yelp with alarm and surge into it, checking for damage.

Along the tunnel, Stan trotted and shook, testing out his returned deer form.

'Grubs and shrubs,' said Doug, the first proper words he'd said in ages. 'It feels grand to have my own feet rather than those twiggy stilts.'

'Count yourself lucky that you experienced such magnificent limbs as mine,' sniffed Stan.

'Maybe the going-haywire part of the ripple is wearing off,' Hedy said to Bess hopefully.

No sooner had she spoken than the air around the bear and the stag began to crinkle, contorting their shapes, pulsing inwards and downwards. *Oh no*, thought Hedy, *they've only just come right!*

Before their eyes, both animals shrank. Stan's antlers dwindled and disappeared, and white spots appeared on his back. Doug's jowls receded, as did the muscly shape of his shoulders.

The ripple in magic faded away, like an earthquake striking and passing. In its wake, Hedy and the others found themselves staring at a trembling fawn and a fuzzy brown bear cub.

Spencer was the first to drop to his knees and coo to the small animals, who rushed over to sniff his hands. He was soon joined by everyone else who jostled for a turn to pet them. Even the usually stern-looking Tempest had a softer expression as Doug nosed her claws.

'You guys are so cute and you're going to come live at *my* house,' Max murmured as he scratched Stan's chin.

'Why your house?' Hedy protested. 'They belong to Grandpa John and Grandma Rose.'

'You can share us,' said Doug in a high-pitched voice. 'I want to go to everybody's house.'

'Me too!' Stan agreed. Like Doug, he sounded like a preschooler.

Simon finally finished inspecting his fallen piano stool. 'It is scratched, but thankfully no fatal damage. You two could have ended me!'

Both little animals froze, chastened, and then they began to cry.

Bess sighed. 'Come on. No one will be able to go to anyone's house unless we get out of this slipway and do what we need to do.'

Their exit to Paris was a long ladder into a dark basement. It was quiet, with a delicious smell lingering in the air – a bit like the kitchen at home when Hedy and Spencer baked bread with Mum, but sweeter. There were racks, trays and large bags of flour neatly stacked on a pallet. They were in a bakery.

It was just as well that Doug and Stan had transformed, Hedy thought, because the ladder would have struggled with their combined adult bodies. Instead, Bess put them over his shoulder to carry them up, one at a time. Jelly was still wobbly on her feet but, going slowly, made her way up the ladder without help.

The two animals were like mischievous three-year-olds in their midst. They sniffed everyone and everything, butted each other with their heads and chased each other around without stopping. Doug not-so-accidentally punctured one of the bags of flour and it burst in a cloud.

'That was Stan,' he said immediately, and then proceeded to roll in the flour, looking like a polar bear cub playing in the snow.

'I feel bad for the bakers who have to clean all that up,' Hedy said as they slipped out of the bakery into the back alley. They'd left behind a terrible mess as well as filching a few baguettes left over from the day before.

Bess shrugged contritely. 'The Sleight owns it, although the workers don't know it. When all this is fixed, we'll make it up to them somehow.' He looked up and around to get his bearings, and then motioned for them all to follow him along the cobblestone alley.

Hedy had never been to Paris before, and she gawped as they stole through the streets.

Throughout the sleeping city, street lamps glowed, archways radiated, and spotlights shone on the roofs of grand stone buildings. Lights were strung through trees, and fountains and statues were illuminated too. Through their adventures, she'd seen enough enlivened statues to imagine spirits might be hiding behind these stone faces that stared beyond the night, into the past.

Bess seemed to be keeping them to the darker streets where he could, but every now and then Hedy could see a river to their right. The River Seine. As they travelled alongside it, she saw bridges glimmering over the water, one after another.

'Is she not *magnifique*?' murmured Simon. 'The

City of Light. So called because she was a beacon of enlightenment, of knowledge.'

'I heard all the lights were because one of the King Louis wanted to make it hard for thugs and thieves to hide in alleyways,' said Bess.

He was deliberately baiting the proud French ghost and a quiet squabble ensued between them, which Hedy ignored. She preferred to take in the chic window displays that they passed. One had candles hanging in an elegant curve like a harp, another had cosmetics arranged like a tiered cake, and a third showed off bicycles strung up with bows on enormous ribbons.

Even the older shopfronts captivated her with their colour and signage. Some words were easy to decode such as *céramiques*, *barbier*, *chocolat*. Hedy tried to figure out the meaning of others by studying what was in the windows. It all helped make her anxiety about the snow globes and her missing family retreat, just a little.

Some streets along, Simon stopped in his tracks, then sank down through a manhole cover.

'What is it, Simon?' Spencer asked.

There was no answer, and Bess kept them moving,

knowing that the unseen tether to Simon's piano stool would eventually drag the ghost along. When at last Simon reappeared, Hedy asked, 'Did you find another slipway?'

'*Non*,' said the ghost. 'It was a way to the catacombs. A city below this city.'

'A city below here? How many people live down there?' Max asked.

Simon chuckled darkly. 'No one *lives* down there.'

Above them, Tempest was flitting from rooftop to rooftop, staying out of sight. She threw down a pellet every now and then, to let them know she was still following them.

'Are we there yet?' asked Doug after a while.

'Not yet,' said Bess, 'just a little further.'

'My paws are tired.'

'My hooves are tired,' added Stan.

The lights of a motor scooter swept by, and Hedy risked a look at its rider out of the corner of her eye. Yes, there it was, a double take at their unusual group – children out so late at night, carrying a stool and with two highly unusual pets. She crouched to pick up Stan. 'I'll carry you for a bit.'

'Not fair!' Doug plonked himself down in the

middle of the pavement. 'What about me? Stan is littlest but I'm little too.'

With a sigh, Bess scooped the bear cub into his arms. 'Trust me, you're not that little,' he grunted.

Their destination was a door that looked completely at odds with the modern shopfronts on either side. It was painted in a messy, joyful riot of colours – bright yellow, pinks, turquoise. The traditional sandstone façade of the building above them was adorned with gigantic sculptures of eyes, a nose and lips. The lips had been placed above the eyes and nose, and all the sculptures hung at wacky angles, as though pinned there by a blindfolded giant playing a party game.

Bess beckoned Tempest down from the roof. He whispered to the gargoyle hastily, and she flapped up towards the first-floor windows.

'Now,' said Bess, 'I believe the person who lives here has a Rosetta Jumbler. But she'll never give it to me, so I've just asked Tempest if she can find a way in to . . . borrow it.'

Hedy's eyebrows shot up. 'Without this person knowing?'

'Now's not the time for an ethical debate, Hedy.

You want to save your family, don't you? If you want to be a treasure hunter one day, you're going to have to be creative. That might include being morally creative.'

'It's a good thing I've given up on the treasure hunter idea then,' Hedy muttered, startling Bess for once. 'Magic just leads to trouble. After we get everyone back safe, I think I'm done with it.'

'Did someone say ethical debate,' Jelly interrupted quietly. 'I'm *great* at those. Either side of an argument too. Whose team am I on?'

There was no time to debate, however. Spencer, who had been keeping an eye on their gargoyle friend, pointed upwards and gasped, 'Tempest just got swallowed by those giant lips!'

## CHAPTER 9

## VIOLETTE

'Bess, what do we do?' Hedy asked.

Spencer edged closer into her side. 'Are we being attacked? Like the magicians were?'

Bess muttered some colourful words under his breath but shook his head. 'I don't think so. But to get Tempest back . . . we're going to have to ask the owner.' He had the look of a man being sentenced as he knocked on the colourful door.

After a few moments a woman's irritated voice on the other side said something in French, most likely telling them it was late and to get lost.

'Violette, it's Bess.'

A muffled tirade poured through the crack in the door. Hedy couldn't understand a word, but Simon whispered, 'Monsieur Bess, is it wise to seek help from someone who thinks you fouler than dog mess on her shoes?'

Bess winced. 'Violette, I have children with me. They need help.'

The castigation abruptly stopped, and then the door opened a sliver. The woman peeked out before she yanked it all the way open. She was in pyjamas and the long, dark hair around her shoulders had small smears of white in it, perhaps plaster.

With narrowed eyes, she said in English, 'Some creature was trying to break into my apartment. I suppose it has something to do with you? And you dare to come here asking me for help?'

'I wouldn't have,' said Bess, 'except that something terrible and . . . *beyond* me has happened. Can you let us in?'

Violette jerked her chin at the children. 'Are they yours?'

'No,' said Bess, and then to Hedy's surprise he added, 'unfortunately.'

'Lucky for you,' she muttered to them all. Peering at Doug, she said, 'What kind of dog is that?'

Doug turned around in Bess's arms and piped up, 'I'm not a dog, I'm a *bear*!'

She may have been determined to find fault with the situation, but Violette couldn't help a honk of utterly shocked amusement. 'Well, in that case.' And she stood aside to let them in.

Inside, it was like stepping into a painter's dream. Every inch of the walls, the ceiling and even the floor was adorned with paint, chalk or charcoal in a chaotic patchwork of images.

'Is this whole place your house?' Spencer asked, awed.

'I live here as caretaker. But it's not only mine,' said Violette. 'It's an art studio for about twenty of us. I'm the only one who lives here, though.'

She led them up the spiral staircase towards her apartment at the very top. Up here, the visual turmoil disappeared. The walls were either white or black, showing off photographs, sketches and sculptures. There was even a neon orange sculpture of a swimming woman suspended from the ceiling.

As he shuffled in, Max yelped. The gigantic eye

sculpture outside was staring at them through the glass. There was a mumbled sound and Violette opened the window. The giant lips descended from above the window and spat something into the room.

'*Cambrioleuse*,' the lips said. One huge eye bore into them and, evidently seeing their confusion, had the lips translate for their benefit, 'Thief.'

It had spat out Tempest. The gargoyle was enraged, and shook out her crumpled wings. 'How dare you!'

Violette stumbled backwards, shocked. After a hasty exchange with the lips in French, she rounded on Bess. 'What was this gargoyle trying to take? Are these children paid actors or something like that? I wouldn't put it past you.'

Bess rubbed his face tiredly. 'Like I said downstairs, something dreadful has happened. And we need your help. We're not travelling with a bear, a fawn and a piano stool for fun.'

Simon must have felt slighted for he poked his head through the wall, and said something contemptuous to Bess that none of them understood except Violette. Although Hedy could tell Violette knew more about magic than the average bog, she didn't seem prepared to see a ghost floating through her wall, and she edged away in the other direction.

Nosing Violette's shin reassuringly, Stan said, 'Don't be scared. He's our friend.'

Simon bowed floridly, speaking to Violette in French. His words eventually coaxed a few hoarse words of greeting from her. She sat gingerly on one of her couches and pulled Stan into her lap, like a child with a soft toy.

'Start at the beginning,' she said to Bess.

The treasure hunter sketched out the highlights for her. Magic going wrong, all magicians throughout the United Kingdom trapped, the children's family vanished.

'*Every* magician?' asked Violette sceptically. 'You exaggerate. It would not be the first time you've spun a tale to trick me.'

'I'm not lying this time, Violette.'

'*This time?*' Hedy looked askance at Bess. 'What did you lie about the other time?'

'Excellent question, thank you,' said Violette with a flat stare.

The tension was so thick that Hedy found herself holding her breath.

Finally, Jelly let out a squeak of delight. '*Oh em gee,*

you two were a couple, weren't you? And you're having your lovers' quarrel now! This is better than TV. Bess, I didn't know you were capable of being someone's boyfriend.'

'Trust me, he is *not*.' Violette rubbed her cheek against little Stan who was falling asleep in her arms. 'Are you, Eugene?'

*Eugene?* Hedy knew that Bess was not the treasure hunter's real name, of course; it was a title that treasure hunters took. But he certainly didn't look like a Eugene.

'What did he do that was so bad?' Jelly pressed, well and truly amused by Bess's discomfort.

'Why don't you tell them, Vee, since you don't trust me with the facts?' Bess said tetchily.

Jelly moved next to Violette and began stroking Stan's back. 'All right, Violette, girl to girl, what did he do?'

'He used me to steal from my father,' said Violette, her face darkening. 'My poor father who day by day was losing his memories and his sense of self. Dementia, you understand? It is awful. He has passed on, liberated from it now.' Doug padded over to her, silently asking to sit in Violette's lap as well. As she went on, the bear cub licked the tears on her cheeks. 'Eugene and I were close, until the day he stole a precious object from my father's house. You know about powerful objects, I suppose? This was one my father had made.'

'I know it didn't seem right to take it without your say-so,' said Bess, 'but, Violette, did you ever bother to really consider whether I'd done the right thing back then? Guess what? I *did* do the right thing! I actually made the world safer by removing *Le Paradoxe* from your father when he was deteriorating. It's safer with the Sleight. You were angry at the unfairness of his condition, and you took it all out on me.'

Hedy had never heard Bess say so much in one go before, nor with such emotion. Before tonight, she'd never considered that he wrestled with the consequences of his treasure hunting.

'What did Bess steal from her father?' Stan whispered to Doug in the painful silence.

Doug shrugged. 'A . . . parrot box?'

'Why would you steal from me again with this gargoyle after what you did?' demanded Violette.

'I didn't think you'd ever agree to handing me something else that had belonged to your father. But this is important. And I'm afraid we don't have time for you to find it in your heart to forgive me.'

From the iciness of Violette's glare, it seemed like the artist and the treasure hunter were at a stalemate. It had to be broken if they were to get anywhere.

As Hedy tried to think of the right thing to say, Spencer asked, 'So your father was a maker? Mrs Pal told us there are makers all around the world, but we've never met any of them.'

'Yes, he was.'

'But didn't you want to follow in his footsteps?' Spencer asked. 'I would. I hope I'm going to be a maker when I grow up.'

'Art is my calling,' said Violette. 'And art reaches many more people than magic. I do not have to hide my work the way my father had to, or the way magicians must. Are you apprenticed to a maker yourself?'

Spencer nodded. 'To Mrs Pal, at the Palisade.'

'Hardly,' scoffed Jelly.

'I am so. Sort of.'

'She gives you broken things.'

'She's letting me try things,' Spencer insisted.

'I met Mrs Pal once,' said Violette. 'She was a very knowledgeable woman, and kind to me as a young girl.

My father respected her. And fixing broken things is a beautiful way to learn.'

'We think she's been trapped like the magicians too,' Spencer frowned. 'Maybe all the makers are.'

Hedy unzipped her backpack and pulled out the snow globes, placing them gently on the coffee table. 'This is our grandfather. And this is his carer, Lark. She was accidentally caught up in whatever happened to Grandpa John.'

With wide eyes, Violette bent closer to look at the snow globes. Different emotions warred on her face. Sadness at their plight, awe at the sight of something so remarkable.

Poor Lark, who yesterday had probably planned to go home and read some magazines or watch a movie, had rolled over in her sleep. Her wooden tree brooch was barely visible, only a speck on her tiny woollen cardigan.

Grandpa John was lying on his back now, perfectly straight. Hedy tried to squash the thought that he was lying in a coffin. Seeing Violette grieve for her late father filled Hedy with a too-early dread that, one day, she too would be mourning her grandparents and parents. It was inevitable. Magic was powerless to stop it. But she had to put that day off for as long as possible.

'Violette, we need to fix them,' said Hedy. 'We need Grandpa John to get our family back. To help Mrs Pal and all the makers. To help the other magicians.'

Max held up his hand with the gauntlet. 'And we have to fix me too.'

'Wouldn't your father help us if he were here?' Hedy asked.

Violette frowned. 'What is it you came for?'

'It's called a Rosetta Jumbler,' said Bess. 'Your father had one. To code and decode his journals and the like. Looks like a glass pyramid.'

'I have it.' Violette looked out the window, weighing things up. Actually, Hedy realized, she was looking at the eye sculpture that had been watching them. Violette tilted her head questioningly at the eye, and it blinked once. She turned back to them. 'I think my father would have helped you.' With a rankled glare at Bess, she added, 'You know, just because I never want to forgive you, doesn't mean I wouldn't do what is right.'

Bess shrugged. 'I excel at bringing out the worst in people.'

'You speak the truth for once,' Violette agreed. She gently slipped Doug and Stan to the floor and got to her feet. 'Wait here.'

A few minutes later, Violette returned with a box. 'Some of my father's things,' she told them, patting the box affectionately.

When Violette lifted the Rosetta Jumbler out of the box, Spencer murmured, 'Yep, Grandpa John definitely had one of those.'

The pyramid was about ten centimetres tall. Embedded at its centre was the nib of a calligraphy pen. Bess explained that the Rosetta Jumbler could code pieces of text with one side of the pyramid, by translating the words into hundreds or thousands of different languages. Another side of the pyramid would reverse the effect.

Spencer held Grandpa John's notebook open flat, while Hedy kept the pyramid steady on top of the left-hand page, the side that had Grandpa John's writing on it.

As Bess lit a candle and brought it closer, Jelly asked, 'So, how many times have you done this before, Bess?'

'Me?' said Bess. 'None. But I've watched someone else do it.'

'Right. Just don't burn the only clue to rescuing our entire family and saving magic.'

Bess gave her a hard stare and then touched the candle flame to one side of the pyramid.

The Rosetta Jumbler seemed to suck the flame into itself, leaving a wisp of smoke rising from the candle wick. Inside the glass, the pen-nib turned incandescent and then light refracted, forming a rainbow that danced over the page.

Before their eyes, the words that had been in countless unfamiliar languages coiled and twitched and then they began to travel. They moved from the left page to the blank right-hand page, settling as Grandpa John's writing in English.

When Hedy flipped the page over, they saw the same thing happening on the next page, and the next . . .

It had worked.

## CHAPTER 10

## THE ROSETTA JUMBLER

'What does it say?' asked Doug.

Stan nosed his way into the centre of the group. 'I want to read!'

'Fawns can't read,' Doug scoffed.

'I can so.' The little deer scanned the words, but quickly became downcast when he couldn't make sense of them.

'It's OK, Stan,' said Spencer, 'you'll be a great reader when you're big. Hedy, what does it say?'

The front of the notebook didn't seem to have any information on what had happened. There were entries about magical artefacts being sold by Mrs Pal, a page about cousin Ewan's talking cockatoos, and the workings of a chess game he was playing against Grandma Rose. It was on the later pages that Hedy found entries relating to where they now found themselves.

She read aloud for the room: '*More and more signs of magic unspooling every day – it's not just me and the house. The Sleight's research makes sense – the Spellbound Tree is failing and it must be relit. We must find a chalkydri. Only it can relight the Tree. It seems we have a month at most.*'

And on another page:

'*Sir Roland's sword is the key to finding the chalkydri. But the key to what door? The Whisper of Paris is rumoured to know more. I must convince him to tell me where to go. To speak with the Whisper, a true magician must pay the one who passes through walls.*'

There was a grumpy postscript in another shade of ink:

'*The Sleight are sending Bess with me. They had the gall to say it was so I don't fall down and break a hip. I'll have to keep him safe while I'm at it. I imagine Hedy could do a better job than the two of us put together. Would much rather travel alone, but I suppose he can carry my bags.*'

'Carry his bags?' huffed Bess. 'Well, I'm glad John thought he could get some use out of me.'

'What's a ch—' Max faltered at the unfamiliar word. 'What's a chalky?'

Hedy checked the notebook. '*Chalkydri.* I've never heard of it.'

'A creature that can eat the fire of the sun,' said Tempest. 'I did not know such a thing was real.'

'Said the talking gargoyle,' murmured Spencer. He quickly hid his grin with a nose-scratch when Tempest glowered at him.

'*Passes through walls.* Is there some French magician who can walk through walls?' Jelly asked.

Violette tapped her chin. 'I don't know any magicians – as I said, that was my father's world.' She nodded in the direction of the eye and lips that hovered curiously by the window. 'Despite the guardians he left me, I never maintained any connections with his business. But it sounds to me like a statue in Montmartre, a well-known character in Paris.'

Hedy could tell that Bess would have liked to set off on their way almost immediately, but everyone was exhausted. Max was almost asleep on the sofa and the rest of them struggled to keep their eyes open too.

Violette finally shepherded the kids to her bed, insisting she would be perfectly happy on the sofa if Doug and Stan curled up with her.

As Hedy drifted off, she heard Violette ask, 'Do you need a blanket, Eugene?'

There was a creak of leather, Bess stretching out on the other sofa. 'No thanks, I have this shawl.'

'That was mine too! I wondered where it went, you—' And she ended with a word in French that Hedy didn't know but whose meaning was clear.

Bess seemed unperturbed. 'It's very warm. I travel everywhere with it. This shawl's been from Greenland to Australia and a hundred places in between.' After a pause, he said, 'Do you want it back?'

'You're *impossible*,' Violette replied, but Hedy had a feeling she was smiling.

The sound of jeers from right outside the window woke them in the morning. When Hedy stumbled into the living room, Violette was sternly calling the giant lips back inside her apartment.

'It's never done that before,' she said. She scolded the lips as they settled belligerently into the corner, grumbling under their breath.

'They are magic,' Tempest pointed out, 'and there is something wrong with magic. My fellow grotesques were also behaving out of character when we departed. What will your neighbours say?'

'I've let them think that the eyes and nose and lips are robotic,' said Violette. 'I suppose they'll think they have malfunctioned. Or perhaps they'll think that it was the artist's intent to throw insults at people walking by.'

Bess had risen early to buy a small mountain of warm, crusty rolls, which they all devoured with butter and jam. Doug tackled breakfast with so much enthusiasm that he turned into a head-to-toe mess of strawberry preserves while Stan fastidiously ate some nuts and fruit.

While they munched, Hedy checked that Grandpa John and Lark were still all right in their snow globes. Nothing had changed, but in the light of day, Hedy could now make out what Lark held in her hand. She squawked around her mouthful of breakfast. 'We had one all along!'

'Had one of what?' said Spencer.

'A Rosetta Jumbler. Look.' Hedy placed Lark's snow globe in the centre of the table and pointed. 'There in Lark's hand. She must have been holding Grandpa John's Jumbler when she was caught up in the snow globe. He used to keep it on his desk.' She paused, puzzled.

'What is it?' Jelly asked.

'Do you think it's weird Lark was holding something from his desk?'

Spencer shrugged. 'In an explosion you'd probably grab anything you could.'

'But why was she in his study with him?'

'Uncle John *did* run off in the middle of the check-up,' said Jelly. 'He's still got the blood pressure thingy on.'

'Or could be the universe playing a practical joke,' said Bess, gulping his black coffee. 'Sod's Law. *Here's what you need, but you can't get to it.*'

'Poor Lark,' said Hedy. 'Stuck like this because the universe wanted to prank us.'

'Happens to me a lot,' said Bess.

For them to get to Montmartre, Violette let them borrow the van that was sometimes used by the artists to transport their works. There weren't enough seats for all of them plus Violette so Bess drove, promising to have it back to her as soon as they could.

Hedy stared out of the windscreen, fascinated by how the city felt familiar and alien at the same time. Buses were a different colour and size but carried people all the same. People walked dogs, but she also saw a few small ones peeking out from large, fashionable bags over the shoulders of fashionable women. And it felt strange for the van to be driving on the other side of the road.

Bess pulled up in a cobblestone street with cafes and ivy prettily climbing the walls. 'It's this square,' he said. 'Humans out. All other beings stay in the van.'

But it wasn't that simple. Doug and Stan began wailing at the notion of being left behind, loudly enough that any passers-by would stop and probably call the police. Tempest insisted she would watch them from the trees to protect them from their own thoughtlessness, and Simon defiantly wafted out of the top of the van, refusing to be the only one missing out.

The square wasn't large. It was bordered by an apartment block on one side, and a sloping street on the other. Wedged between them was a stone wall, and in that wall was the statue Violette had spoken of.

It looked exactly as if a larger-than-life man were stepping out of the wall. A leg, two hands, shoulders and the face of a middle-aged man cast in bronze seemed to emerge from the stonework. The rest of him was apparently stuck on the other side. The lower of his two hands was shiny, buffed by years of visitors taking hold of it. It reminded Hedy of the golden hand at Hoarder Hill, leading to the attic's secret room.

'Does he talk or something?' Spencer asked Bess as they watched a few visitors posing for pictures with the statue.

'Let's hope so,' said Bess, 'if we want to get information out of him.'

Satisfied with their photos, the tourists began making their way out of the square. Puzzled looks came over them, however, as they spotted Max with the steel gauntlet sitting on a piano stool, and a bear cub nosing the trees and planters dotting the square.

'Is this your *bear*?' asked one of the tourists, pointing at Doug.

'He's a Bulgarian Bear Hound,' Jelly said, so casually that even Hedy took a moment to realize that her cousin was making it up. 'A dog breed groomed to look like a bear. Doesn't he look just like a teddy?'

Behind her, Hedy and Spencer shuffled closer together to hide Stan from view in Hedy's jacket. He would be harder to pass off as a Dutch Deer Dog or whatever Jelly rattled off the top of her head.

'I am *not* a dog!' Doug complained.

The tourist's eyes widened and she spun to stare at the bear cub who was eyeing her so crossly.

Hedy forced out a stiff laugh and said, 'Good one, Max.' She jerked her chin in Max's direction. 'He's learning ventriloquism.'

'Don't get too close to our dog,' Jelly babbled. 'He's been sniffing every dog poop we've passed. Unless you're OK with getting dog poop on you?'

Unfortunately, even that didn't seem to turn off the tourist and she opened her mouth to ask another question. Without warning, there was a flapping noise in the air above them and a voice shouting, 'Bat! Get away!'

Shrieking, the tourist and her companions threw their hands over their heads and ran from the square as the flapping creature swooped at them.

When they had disappeared down the hill, Tempest alighted on the statue's outstretched hand, very pleased with herself for scaring the tourists away. 'Good. They seemed like they were going to be here for far too long and who knows if they're working for someone. Now, how do we wake this bronze fellow up?'

Hedy and Spencer shook both hands of the statue. They showed him Grandpa John and Lark in the snow globes and pleaded for help. Simon tried talking to the statue in French. Bess even hoisted up Max to wave the gauntlet about and touch it to the statue's outstretched hands and face. None of it drew a reaction.

'Are you sure this is the right man?' Max asked.

'He fits the description,' said Bess, but he was beginning to sound worried.

Tempest grunted. 'There is something irregular about this statue, I can feel it.'

'Is there something or someone hidden behind him?' Spencer wondered.

Simon floated in close. 'Allow me.' He pushed himself against the stone wall but instead of disappearing through it, he hovered there for a few moments, his face growing more and more determined. At last he backed up. 'I cannot get through. It is most peculiar; I have never been stopped by a wall before.'

That was an encouraging sign, at least. Hedy read from Grandpa John's notebook once again.

'*The Whisper of Paris is rumoured to know more. I must convince him to tell me where to go. To speak with the Whisper, a true magician must pay the one who passes through walls.*'

'So we need a magician,' said Spencer.

'You didn't happen to bring John's wand with you,

did you?' Bess asked.

Hedy shook her head.

Spencer fumbled with his bag to pull out his skyskepnur. 'But I brought this.'

Jelly began counting on her fingers. 'We have a tiny magician in a snow globe. Spencer's mostly useless cloud rod – sorry, Spence. The gauntlet that won't come off, and we're travelling with a ghost. How much more proof of magic does he need?'

'I guess they're only proof that we *have* magical objects,' said Hedy, 'not proof that we can do magic.' She re-read the words. '*To speak with the Whisper, a true magician must pay the one who passes through walls.*'

'What about this?' Bess tried slipping some money into the statue's hands but coins and notes alike dropped to the ground.

'But Bess, you're not a magician,' said Max, 'you're a bog like us.'

There was a pause and then Jelly cleared her throat awkwardly. She asked for a euro coin from Bess and then she approached the bronze man in the wall.

'What are you doing?' Spencer asked.

Jelly shook her hand out to relax it. 'Probably nothing. But if it's something, don't freak out.'

## CHAPTER 11

### THE WHISPER

With the coin in her palm, Jelly reached out to clasp the lower hand of the bronze man. All sound in the square was dampened at once, like a giant blanket had been thrown over them. Molten bronze began leaching from the statue's hand to hers, sweeping down her fingertips and over the knuckles towards her wrist.

It stopped there. The statue's hand twitched and suddenly gripped its fingers around her. When it let her go, it held the coin. The hand deftly flipped the coin over its own knuckles, and then with a graceful swish, opened its fingers to reveal an empty palm.

*Click.* The statue's other hand, much higher up the wall, snapped its fingers. It proudly wiggled the coin that had inexplicably appeared up there.

'How did you *do* that?' Spencer gasped, staring at Jelly's bronze hand.

Jelly was hardly ever lost for words, but she struggled to find the right ones now. 'Well . . . I . . .'

'Are you a magician?' Hedy whispered, stunned.

The statue clicked his fingers for their attention again, pointed at each of them, and grasped Jelly's hand. It was asking them to join up, to form a line.

Once they were holding hands, the statue suddenly stepped back through the wall, dragging them with him – Jelly, Hedy, Max and Spencer.

To Hedy, the sensation was like the sharp smack of water when belly-flopping into a pool. It stung for a moment, but she'd plunged through to the other side by the time the sting really registered.

They stumbled into a place that was like a mirror image of the square they'd been in, only here everything was bronze. The paving stones and cobbles, the trees and street lamps, even the apartment building on one side. Everything except the man now regarding them.

He looked just like the statue brought to life – larger than normal, with the same receding hairline, narrow face and suit.

'My god, you have the sword!' he exclaimed, staring at the blade that had emerged in Max's hand. 'Who are you?'

There were only the four of them. Bess, who had been holding Max's gauntleted hand, hadn't come through the wall. Each of them said their name in turn.

It did not seem to be what the tall man wanted to hear. 'The magicians of France all lie sleeping. Who *are* you to have this sword in your possession?'

'We're here to ask for help—' began Hedy, but the tall man cut her off.

'That one is a *magicienne*, I can see,' he said, gesturing at Jelly's hand that was still bronzed. 'That is why I granted you passage. But you seek my help? I do not know you, you are not from here. I do not know your pedigree, your provenance, your accomplishments.'

'Excuse me?' muttered Jelly. 'Pedigree? What are we, dogs or something?'

Hedy racked her brains to decipher what this man needed to hear. Who were they? Why would he believe they belonged to this world?

Spencer suddenly blurted out, 'We're the family of the Amazing John Sang. His grandchildren, his great-niece and great-nephew. We have battled mythical beasts and performed many great feats far beyond this realm. We're the Hoarder Hill Four.'

Hedy gaped at her younger brother.

'The Hoarder Hill Four?' repeated the man.

Jelly was the first to catch on and play along. 'Yeah, that's right. The Hoarder Hill Four. We, uh, found Verdandi's Loom about a year ago. And Hedy is the bearer of a magician's map.'

'And before that,' said Spencer, 'we saved our grandmother who'd been trapped in a magic box for thirty years.'

'And we've met giants,' added Max.

The tall man pursed his lips, thinking hard. 'I believe I have heard inklings of these exploits. I know of the Amazing John Sang, of course.'

'Well,' said Hedy, reaching into her backpack, 'this is him now.' She showed the man the snow globe with Grandpa John sleeping inside. 'He was preparing to come find you for help about what you said: about all the magicians sleeping.' When the tall man bent to examine the snow globe, she asked, 'Who are you, please, sir?'

'I am the Whisper of Paris,' he said. 'A confessor to magicians. The one to whom they entrust their riddles and confidences.'

'Can you fix him? It's not only our grandfather trapped like this.' She drew Lark's snow globe from the bag. 'Our parents have disappeared too. The British Museum in London vanished with them.'

He shook his head sympathetically. 'I am confessor, but my magic is not of the kind to contend with *this* enchantment. You need a powerful magician, but as I said, the magicians of France are all overcome. They sleep like the princess who pricked her finger on the last spindle in the land. They need saving themselves.'

It was like a boot heel grinding out a tiny bud of hope in Hedy before it had had time to grow. 'Are none awake to help us?'

'None. What about your homeland?'

'The magicians of Britain suffer the same thing.'

The Whisper narrowed his eyes at Jelly. 'Not all of them.'

'Whoa, it wasn't me!' Jelly protested, hands up. 'I don't have a clue why I'm not trapped.'

Hedy took a deep breath. No magicians in France to free their family. What were they supposed to do now?

'This sword?' she asked, pointing at Max's hand. 'What is it? Why was our grandfather coming to find you?'

The Whisper took a seat on a planter. 'An age ago, the sword belonged to one who pledged to protect the tree that is the fountainhead of magic. The Spellbound Tree.'

'What does fountainhead mean?' Max asked.

'Source. It's the source of magic.'

'*One* tree is the source of magic?'

'In a sense. Just as a river can be traced back to a stream, and that stream can be traced back to a spring that starts its life as a trickle among some rocks. It is no ordinary tree, of course. In some ways it is only posing as a tree, so that our small minds may comprehend it. Perhaps its true form is actually something different. Well, in an earlier age, it was decided that the tree needed protecting. Magic was endangered, you see, by a war between magicians and non-magicians.'

Hedy and the others nodded. They'd all learnt about this old conflict on their last adventure.

'The fighting came to an end when, on the verge of annihilation, magicians promised to work in the shadows.'

'The Pact,' said Hedy.

'Indeed – when the Pact was agreed to, the non-magicians demanded the tree's protectors put aside their weapons. I believe this sword is one of those weapons. In these times, you would think of it as a magician surrendering his or her wand. The Spellbound Tree was allowed to live on, untended by protectors, but unharmed by non-magicians. Something is happening now, though. Something is wrong with the Spellbound Tree. For weeks, magicians the world over have been sharing stories of magic going wrong. Even my magic is deteriorating – your friend was left behind on the other side of the wall.'

Hedy slipped Grandpa John's notebook from her waistband and flipped through it. '*The Spellbound Tree is failing and it must be relit*,' she read. '*We must find a chalkydri. Only it can relight the Tree.*'

'What happens if it isn't fixed?' Max asked. 'Will I be stuck with this on my hand for ever, or will it drop off?'

The Whisper bent low to bring his face level with

Max's. 'Young man, a world without magic is what will happen. Is that what you want?'

'None of us want that,' said Spencer.

*A world without magic would be a world without a whole heap of problems*, Hedy thought. Then she squirmed at her own disloyalty. 'Is the British Museum magical? Is that why it disappeared with our family?'

'An institution like that is bound to have enchantment within it,' said the Whisper. 'Historical, dormant magic perhaps.'

'What'll happen to magicians if there's no magic?' asked Jelly.

'I do not know. Perhaps they die.'

Hedy grabbed Jelly's hand and gave it a squeeze. The Whisper had said 'they', as though avoiding the fact that 'they' now included Jelly.

'Or perhaps magic simply dies away,' he continued, 'like a language one used to be able to speak.'

'Are the magicians trapped and sleeping because magic is going wrong?' said Hedy.

'I think not. Otherwise, this young *magicienne* – Jelly – would not be standing here. I think instead that someone has targeted every magician they knew of. So that no one is left to save the Spellbound Tree.'

Hedy, Spencer, Jelly and Max shared a look and a thought. *We're the ones left.*

'My grandfather wrote that the sword is the key to finding the chalkydri,' said Hedy. 'What is it?'

'A creature of many hues,' said the Whisper, 'said to have twelve wings, the head of a crocodile and the body of a lion.'

'All that and it eats the fire of the sun,' murmured Jelly. 'Is it just me or does it sound completely bananas, and too big to fit in the van, *and* kind of terrifying?'

Hedy completely agreed with her cousin but she tried to keep on track. 'How do we find it, sir?'

'A powerful being such as the chalkydri had to be kept safe from the wrong people,' said the Whisper. 'If non-magicians were to unleash a chalkydri's power maliciously, it could destroy the Tree instead of reviving it. I've heard that the carousel of lost creatures can take a magician to the chalkydri. Once there, you will need the sword to release it.'

'And then we need to get it to the Spellbound Tree? Is that in Paris?'

'No. Our world adjoins the isle of the Spellbound Tree in many places, but it is not *here*. The only other whisper I have heard is that the chalkydri must read the Book of Fire, and then it may cross over.'

'Book of Fire? Where is that?'

'That I do not know.' He clucked in frustration. 'Although my magic cannot help you, I will ask others in the bones of the city to aid you if they can.'

He cocked his head as though hearing something. 'Our time is over. You must return now, lest you be turned to bronze yourselves,' he said. 'Link up again please. *Magicienne* Jelly, you will need to present me your marked hand.'

## CHAPTER 12

## DODO MANÈGE

Lurching through the wall, they bowled into Bess. He must have been pacing in front of it the whole time. The bronze statue had frozen in place again, and nothing appeared untoward about the square except them.

'Nice of you to come back for me,' he said dryly, getting to his feet and helping them stand.

'It wasn't our fault you were left behind,' said Max. 'The Whisper said it's because magic is wonky.'

'That old excuse?' Bess looked them over. 'Is everyone all right?'

The molten bronze that had marked Jelly's hand had mostly disappeared, although it looked like she had bronze polish on her middle fingernail. Besides that, they were unchanged and all accounted for.

Doug and Stan came scampering down the slope, yelling in glee and ignoring the hissed reprimands of Tempest.

'I've been trying to keep them quiet and out of sight,' the gargoyle complained, 'but they stir up trouble in each other.'

'I think we'd all best get out of sight,' said Bess. He indicated the windows of the apartment block bordering the square. 'I've seen a few faces looking out of the windows and I worry about who's watching and how much they've seen.'

In the safety of the van, they caught everyone up on their encounter with the Whisper and his instruction to take Sir Roland's sword to the carousel of lost creatures.

'Carousel of lost creatures? That's exactly what he said?' asked Bess. He looked something up on his phone. 'I guess this must be it.'

Hedy leant forwards. 'What is?'

'The Dodo Manège,' said Bess. 'His words describe

it almost perfectly. It's a children's carousel where the animals you ride on are all extinct or at risk of becoming so.'

'Is that the sort of thing all Besses should know about?'

'It helps that I've been to Paris a few times before.'

'You didn't know about the passer through the wall, though.'

Bess coughed, embarrassed. 'I rode on the Dodo Manège with Violette once.'

'Like a date or something?' Hedy laughed. She had come across many extraordinary things on their adventures but Bess out on a date seemed more unbelievable than any of them.

The treasure hunter pointedly changed the subject. 'Jelly, why didn't you tell anyone you're a magician?'

That unleashed a barrage of questions from everyone that made Jelly cover her head with her hands. 'I know, I'm sorry. But it's a super-new thing, and I don't know what I'm going to do about it because I don't know if I even *want* to become a magician.'

'Are you kidding?' Max screeched. 'Of course you want to become a magician.'

'No, *you* want to become a magician. And don't

forget what the Whisper said. Someone targeted all the known magicians. I don't want to be on someone's hit list!'

A nagging question clicked into place for Hedy. 'That's why you had that mysterious secret meeting with Grandpa John, isn't it? I knew that story about a recommendation for school was fake!'

Jelly dropped her head on to Hedy's shoulder, contrite. 'Seriously, one hundred per cent sorry. I didn't know how you'd take it. You're like the chosen one around here.'

'What about me?' bristled Spencer.

'Nope, it's Hedy if it's going to be anyone. Remember what your grandad wrote in his notebook, that she could probably do a better job than him and Bess together?' Jelly sighed. 'If Uncle John was less weird about doing magic, maybe I'd have a better idea of whether I want to get into the whole thing. Plus, lucky me, I bet that's why I was so sick when the ripple of wonkiness happened.'

'When did you find out?' Hedy asked. 'And how did you find out?'

Jelly blushed and pointed to her forehead. 'It was the school dance three weeks ago. And of course on the morning of the dance, I got this huge spot right in the middle of my forehead, one of those massive ones that waves at people and tells them its life story, you know? So I was staring at it in the mirror, swearing at it, and right before my eyes it disappeared. Gone from my forehead.' She grimaced. 'And one second later, it came up on my chin. So I didn't make it disappear, I just moved it. I called Mum to watch me do it, to make sure I wasn't imagining it.'

'Are you pulling our legs?' asked Spencer, suspicious.

'If I was pulling your leg,' she said, 'I wouldn't make up something that was boring *and* humiliating. Your grandad said sometimes magical ability comes through in puberty, so I guess that's the ultimate combination of both.' She glanced at Hedy. 'You still don't trust magic though. You're in the "anti" brigade. Are you anti me?'

'Course not. Moving spots isn't a bad thing to be able to do,' Hedy pointed out, 'if you can move them somewhere out of sight.'

'If I could move them to someone else, like Bridget, this total hyena at my school, *that* would be magic worth having,' said Jelly. 'What do you think I should do? Become a magician?'

Hedy didn't have an answer for her. As the boys made the case for following in Grandpa John's footsteps, Hedy stared through the windscreen, trying to make sense of the news.

It seemed horribly full of herself to agree with Jelly's comment about her being 'the chosen one around here'. The truth, however, was that it *was* a shock to learn Jelly was the one in their generation with a magician's gift. Wasn't Hedy the one who had pulled off so many remarkable feats in the last few years? It would even make more sense if it had been Spencer, since he was so obsessed with creating magical objects and was John Sang's grandson. *Be careful what you wish for*, Dad sometimes told her. Maybe turning her back on magic had prompted magic to turn its back on her.

As she mulled this over, her eyes slid across someone hopping out of a car down the street. A split second later her mind caught up. The bald head shaped like an egg, the faded corduroy jacket, the hunched shoulders.

'Shhhh!' she said, putting her hand over Max's mouth. 'It's Greedy Grutz! Look! What's he doing here in Paris?'

The van fell quiet. 'Stay out of sight,' said Bess,

'behind the seats. He's not alone.'

A couple of motorbikes slunk into the street too. Their riders parked and joined Mr Grutz who had walked into the square.

'Is he following us?' Max whispered. Stan and Doug began whimpering.

'I'll bet your festering fish burger hand that he is,' said Jelly.

Simon, who kept himself at the back of the van so as not to accidentally touch anyone, said, 'I shall see if I can hear what they say.'

The ghost faded from view. Bess kept an eye on Mr Grutz and the motorcyclists in his side mirror. 'They're in the square, but I don't think they know what they're supposed to do.'

Simon reappeared. 'They are searching for you. And they too are looking for the Spellbound Tree.'

'Shall I attack?' Tempest offered at once.

But Bess switched the keys in the ignition. 'No. We just try to get a head start.'

The carousel they were looking for was inside the grand botanical garden along the Seine, the Jardin des Plantes.

Bess swerved into the closest empty spot he could find and bustled them out, saying he'd rather catch a parking ticket than dally for too long. Seeing Mr Grutz had put him on edge.

'First he has a tool to break the Obscurity over John's house,' said Bess. 'And now he shows up in Paris, chasing you lot? I'm sure he must be with BUTTS.'

Spencer and Max started sniggering. 'Did you say Mr Grutz is with butts?' Spencer asked.

'There's a group known as the Ban on Unnatural Taboo Thaumaturgy,' said Bess. 'They give the rest of us bogs a bad name. See themselves as the police of the Pact. I call them BUTTS. From what I can see, they relish an excuse to go after magicians.' He hauled the piano stool out of the van. 'Simon, you're coming with us in case we need a translator. If anyone asks us about Doug and Stan, we're taking them to become new residents at the zoo in the gardens.' Bess glared at the two little animals for using tears to blackmail their way into joining them again. 'It's not a great cover story but it'll have to do since you won't stay in the van.'

'What does "resident" mean?' Stan asked, eyes wide.

'Lion-food?' whispered Doug.

'It might, if you don't behave,' Bess warned. 'Don't

get into trouble, otherwise we might in fact leave you at the front gates.'

'I shall survey from above,' said Tempest. 'Try not to get separated again.' She looked up and down the street then launched into the air when the coast was clear.

Luckily, it was an overcast morning so the park was not as busy as it might have been on a sunny day. They hurried along the gravel path too quickly to admire the flower beds and tree-lined walkways that stretched away from the river. Hedy did her best to ignore the curious stares of people around them, and held Stan tightly to her chest.

Before long, they heard music like that of an old-style circus – a hurdy-gurdy melody that was soon punctuated by children's voices and the clank of moving machine parts. In such extensive grounds, the carousel seemed small and hidden away. But its simple sign, painted with a hard-eyed bird, proclaimed they had found the Dodo Manège.

## CHAPTER 13

## LOST CREATURES

'Simon,' said Hedy softly, 'what does *manège* mean?'

The ghost had made himself invisible, and the only way Hedy knew he was close was the cooling of the air by her right ear.

'When I was alive, it meant a school for teaching horses and their riders.' There was a baffled pause. 'Perhaps the meaning has changed for I do not see a single horse on this machine.'

Small children rode strange creatures in a gentle circuit. Among the more familiar giant panda and gorilla were a triceratops, peculiar horned giraffes, a large bird like an ostrich and, of course, a dodo. The centre and ceiling panels of the carousel were painted with trees and other wild creatures.

Bess bought tickets from the small booth nearby but said, 'We should wait for some of these people to clear out.'

Hedy wandered over to a red wooden sign by the fence that described the animals. It was in French, but she tried to pick out words here and there about the creatures she'd never heard of before. The carousel went through three rounds of visitors before they had it to themselves. Bess approached the young woman running the carousel while they each chose an animal to ride. She seemed puzzled by them, probably because they were much older than her usual customers. Hedy took one of the giraffe-like creatures, which she'd just learnt was called a sivatherium, and coaxed Doug and Stan on to the back of a horned turtle.

Thanks to Simon whispering in Bess's ear, the treasure hunter was able to have a stilted conversation with the carousel woman, and found out that the man who ordinarily ran the carousel was not there. 'This young lady said he came down ill,' Bess said darkly as he leant against a giant panda. 'Maybe he's a magician. I'd say she's even more of a bog than we are, though. When I mentioned the Spellbound Tree, she drew a blank.'

'What do we do?' Spencer asked. 'Does Jelly have to do magic here?'

'The Whisper said the carousel of lost creatures can take a magician to the chalkydri,' Hedy reminded them. 'But we need the sword to release it.' She turned to Jelly and Max. 'You two had better stick together.'

The carousel began to whirl, its music playing over the creaking wooden boards. They rose and fell with the animals but nothing in the least bit magical showed itself. Around and around they went and Hedy began to worry. *Perhaps the Whisper heard wrong.*

'Faster!' Doug cried out, as they waited for something to happen.

Stan shushed him with a nudge. That led to a shoving match which in turn led to the two animals tumbling off the back of the horned turtle. Paws and hooves a-tangle, the pair began to call each other names.

'Hog's breath!'

'Skunk bum!'

'Weasel wart!'

They chased each other around the platform, ignoring the hissed reprimands of everyone. Hedy sensed the carousel manager gawking at them. In all likelihood, she'd never seen talking animals before.

When Stan sent Doug flying with a mischievous kick of his legs, the bear cub almost sailed right off the carousel. Jelly reached out with a yell. The distance was too great; she should have missed Doug, but somehow his trajectory changed just a few degrees. Enough for Jelly to catch him, and haul him on to her ride, a sivatherium like Hedy's.

'Did you just do magic?' said Hedy, mouth agape.

Jelly looked at her guiltily.

There was a clanging noise, louder than any they had heard before. The music of the carousel lost its tinny tone, rising as if their ears had suddenly cleared and a circus orchestra was playing all around them, crystal clear.

The carousel itself began to pick up speed. Faster and faster whirled the platform so that the trees of the park, the booth and the young woman became lost to view. The Jardin des Plantes turned into nothing more than streaks speeding past, and something happened to the painted panels at the centre of the carousel. The vista took on depth; the painted trees seemed to recede and grow and multiply, becoming a great wood opening inward and broadening around them at the same time.

Hedy suddenly shot upwards as her sivatherium changed from a rigid carousel ride to a live beast of flesh and blood, three metres tall. She flung her arms around the creature's long neck to hold on, marvelling at the feel of fur in her hands. And then its smell hit her nose, a mixture of vegetation and . . . dung. She tried not to breathe through her nose.

Around her, the others looked as astonished as she felt.

Jelly was up high on her sivatherium with Doug.

Hedy almost fell off her ride when she saw Spencer clutching Stan on a whopping, horned and frill-necked triceratops. It clacked its beak and swooshed its tail from side to side, whacking bushes in the process.

Max was on a far smaller lost creature. The red sign had called it a thylacine, which looked like a cross between a wolf and a tiger. 'Where's Bess?' he asked.

Hedy swung around. Max was right. The treasure

hunter wasn't with them. 'He must've been left behind.'

'Again? He's *always* getting lost.'

'He chose a giant panda,' Spencer said in a low voice. 'Not extinct yet. Maybe that's the reason.'

'Why are you talking so quietly?' Jelly asked.

'I don't want to spook this guy,' said Spencer, pointing at his triceratops. He looked around at the trees surrounding them. 'How the heck do we find the chalkydri in all of this?'

As soon as he mentioned the chalkydri, the sword-blade slid out from the pommel in Max's gauntlet. It glowed as brightly as a neon sign.

Without being told, their animals moved off, placidly heading towards the sound of crashing water. They obviously knew where they were going. Hedy hoped they would be as sure of their direction on the way back.

Before long, they arrived at a small lake. The water was shallow and perfectly clear. Hedy could see the bottom dappled with pebbles of incredible colour: musk pink, maroon, teal, mustard, azure.

The noise the animals had followed was a waterfall. It gushed over a cliff about thirty metres high, hitting the lake below. The animals all waded in, even Max's thylacine, until they were nearly beneath the waterfall itself. Thankfully, it wasn't deep.

'Is the chalkydri here?' Hedy asked her sivatherium. It only blinked in response.

'What's that?' Spencer asked, pointing.

Beyond the falling sheets of water shone something like a small disco light. Coloured light. *A creature of many hues*, Hedy recalled the Whisper saying.

She nudged her sivatherium a little closer, and tried to put her hand through the waterfall. But there was a sort of invisible barrier in front of it, and Hedy couldn't even get close enough to wet her fingers.

'Max?' Hedy beckoned her young cousin and the thylacine obediently waded closer to the waterfall. 'The Whisper said we need the sword.'

'Do I have to battle something?' Max asked, eyes turning to saucers. 'I don't want to fight a crocodile or a lion!'

'Or a mash-up of them both,' muttered Spencer.

'Calm down,' said Hedy, trying to steady her own nerves. 'The Whisper said we need the sword to *release* it, not fight it. We're right here with you.'

'I'll fight it for you, Max,' Doug offered, but

Jelly shushed him.

With a quivering breath, Max leant over and used two hands to raise the tip of the luminous sword. Unlike Hedy's hand, whatever was shielding the waterfall didn't stop it. It pierced through, into the waterfall. Like a curtain parting, the plummeting water peeled back to reveal a shallow cave behind it.

About halfway up the cave wall hung a nest. It was pendant-shaped, about ten centimetres tall, woven from grass and twigs. And in its opening, a small creature blazed with all the colours of the rainbow.

'We found it,' Spencer said softly.

'Incredible,' said Jelly. 'I wish I had my sunglasses though. This little guy's shine is super intense. How do we get it down?'

'Come here, Chalky!' Stan called from the triceratops.

Hedy raised an eyebrow at him. 'Chalky?'

Whether it was Stan's tone or some affinity for the sword, the little creature leapt from the nest, dropping a few metres to land on Sir Roland's blade. It chirruped at them and let some of its glow die away, like a light globe with a dimmer switch. Then it scampered down the blade to the hilt of the sword.

Just as Tempest had described, it had a reptilian

head on the body of a lion. But it was about as big as a teacup. Different colours stippled its fur and scaled head, as though it had been dropped into a tray of paint in art class. There were no wings, but Hedy could see small nubs along its back and had a strong suspicion that one day wings would sprout from them.

'It seems like a baby,' she said. She clicked her fingers at Chalky lightly, and it bounded from the sword to her hand, sniffing her and tasting her knuckles with a swipe of its tongue. When the creature let out a shot of green fire, they all flinched.

'If this is a baby, I hope its mama isn't nearby and thinking to barbecue us,' said Jelly.

But before they had time to wonder if another full-grown chalkydri existed and was coming to attack them, a voice said out of nowhere, 'Off you get. Every one of you.'

## CHAPTER 14

## LA SEINE

With a lurching sensation, they found themselves back on the twirling Dodo Manège carousel that was rapidly losing speed. Their animals were shrinking. The vista of trees at the centre of the carousel was fading to two-dimensional paint as the carousel slowed down. Streaks whizzing past them turned back into a booth, park benches, the young woman looking perplexed at her fistful of money that had convinced her to terminate the ride . . . and a hunch-shouldered man in a faded red corduroy jacket.

Mr Grutz. He was flanked by two men with the

same serious expression as his. And between them, they held Bess.

'Where's John Sang?' said Mr Grutz.

'Bess?' Hedy called out.

The treasure hunter's eyes flickered as he caught sight of Chalky on Hedy's shoulder. *Go!* he mouthed.

Hedy shook her head. She didn't want to leave the one grown-up they could trust here.

Mr Grutz grated, 'You're all coming with us.'

'Oh no we're not,' Jelly exploded. 'Hold your horses!' she said to Hedy and the others. Face twisted with intense concentration, Jelly flung an arm forwards, and the animal rides came back to life.

Hedy felt herself rising from the ground as her sivatherium shot up beneath her. She grabbed Chalky from her shoulder and shoved it down into her sweater. The last thing they needed was to lose their key to saving magic. Her sivatherium stomped off the groaning carousel platform, forcing the stunned Mr Grutz and his henchmen back.

Jelly's beast was right next to her. 'Don't fall my down!' she heard Doug whimper, words muddled in his fright.

To her right, Max's thylacine raced ahead. Behind

her was the snorting and clacking of a triceratops beak, and even in the hubbub she heard one of the henchmen let loose a string of curses at the sight of a massive dinosaur shambling in his direction.

A hand yanked at her leg, almost pulling her off balance. It was Mr Grutz trying to drag her down, ordering his companions to lend him a hand. But they had their hands full with Bess who was trying to wrench free. Hedy shouted and kicked as hard as she could. Mr Grutz lost hold of her leg and Hedy felt her sivatherium stretch its legs in a gallop not seen in millennia.

With startled screams at their approach, and baffled shouts in their wake, their race through the garden was no secret getaway. Besides, Hedy was clutching Stan on the back of a giraffe-antelope with massive horns. Even if they'd been standing still, they wouldn't have escaped attention.

'They've still got Bess!' Spencer yelled out as he caught up. 'And we left Simon behind. How do we turn these around?'

'I made them understand we wanted to be somewhere else,' said Jelly, 'but I don't know how to steer them!'

Hedy patted her sivatherium's neck to get its attention, maybe persuade it to change direction. It snorted but otherwise ignored her. 'Where are we going?'

Jelly made a face. 'I don't know that either!'

'Gate!' Max called out.

He was right. Up ahead, people were milling around a statue just inside a handsome gate with gold-tipped posts. The garden visitors scattered as their pack bore down and thundered past, on to the street.

Bicycles, cars and buses screeched and swerved, then came to a standstill – all except for a couple of motor scooters headed for them across the intersection. The way they accelerated into the fray made it clear that they were coming for them.

'They must be with Greedy Grutz,' said Hedy.

Perhaps sensing the new danger, the animals took off to the left. Pedestrians flung themselves out of the way as extinct wildlife dashed towards them.

'Sorry!' Hedy shouted helplessly as they passed by.

Sirens wailed in the distance, but more worrying was the buzz of the motor scooters drawing closer and closer. When the riders drew level to flank the children, one of them lifted her visor and shouted, 'Stop!' She was English, not French.

Spencer tugged at his triceratops's frill and the dinosaur swung its great horns threateningly at the riders on either side, forcing them to veer away. They skidded and fishtailed, only narrowly avoiding cars.

Would the animals keep running in a mindless stampede until exhausted? Hedy wondered. However they were navigating, at least they were staying together. But for how long? Flashing lights and the seesaw siren of a police car sped towards them up ahead while the hum of motor scooters was behind.

The River Seine ran to their right, and a bridge crossing was not far. As though sensing captors closing in, the animals changed course and headed straight for the bridge.

Fear and exhilaration scrambled through Hedy, making her burst out in irrational laughter as they began crossing the river.

'Why are you laughing?' Spencer demanded.

Hedy jerked her chin in the direction of an island in the middle of the Seine. It was dominated by a cluster of pale towers and buttresses, braced with scaffolding. Notre Dame Cathedral. 'At least we're sightseeing.'

Stan peered around Hedy's waist. 'The bad people are coming.'

At that moment, an aggressive car driving in the opposite direction tried to bully its way through and blasted its horn. Hedy's sivatherium was spooked and it reared with a shudder. Unbalanced and unthinking, Hedy flung her arm out.

Stan slipped from her grasp, landing on the hard road of the bridge.

Hedy yelled at her creature, but it kept galloping on. *I can't let them get Stan!* she thought. But how could she get it to turn around? She stretched forwards as far as she could, just reaching the ear of the sivatherium, and tugged on it. It was irritated enough to slow and hook its head around, but she couldn't compel it back along the bridge.

Stan lay limp and unmoving. The scooters zigzagged through cars, drawing close. At the neck of her sweater, Chalky poked out its head and warbled its little chirruping noise. Just when Hedy wondered if she should dismount, four strange creatures plunged out of the sky.

One of them was Tempest, grasping Simon's piano stool. Hedy had never seen the other three before. They were grotesques of different sorts – a long-beaked one, one with a face like a lion, and one that was so worn by time and the elements that it didn't have much of a face at all. They lunged for the riders, using their claws and beaks and hard stone wings to bite and knock them.

Tempest plucked the fawn from the road, lay him on the stool, and with the faceless grotesque took to the air again. 'Retreat!' she croaked at Hedy as she flapped overhead. 'They may not provide cover for long.'

Perhaps the sivatherium understood Tempest better than it did Hedy, for it took off towards the far bank of the river once more. Chalky kept up its twittering song as they galloped.

The grotesques harried the motor scooter riders, but they weren't big enough to stop the police car that was headed after them. As Hedy – the last one in the group – closed in on the end of the bridge, she heard voices singing. The sound came from beside and below the bridge.

Without warning, a great wave shot up from the Seine and broke upon the bridge. It made the cars skid to a stop, and jolted the motor scooters over on their sides. Another wave followed the first, and then another. Over the top of frothing water, Hedy could see the grotesques flying away from their skirmish.

When Hedy joined the others, she turned for a better look.

'It's the faces on the side of the bridge that are singing,' said Max.

He was right. Stone faces decorated the side of the bridge from one bank to the other and they were all singing. Hedy couldn't understand a thing except the words, 'La Seine'.

Jelly jabbed a finger out to the river. 'Who's she?'

Half emerged from the water's surface was a woman seemingly sculpted out of the river. Long hair of reeds, limbs and skin of muddy green water. She gestured at the bridge again and again. She was the one creating the waves that had petrified the drivers up there.

A tiny scrap of Greek mythology rustled in Hedy's mind. *Naiad*, a river nymph. When the woman of water turned her head in their direction, Hedy had a feeling they were looking at the spirit of the River Seine. Chalky's croon beneath her chin had a satisfied sort of tone. Had La Seine done this because of their new little friend?

As the stone faces sang on, time seemed to slow. The wave that rose over the bridge stopped mid-air.

Eyes still upon them, the naiad turned her hands over to fashion something out of her river: an image of an immense tree with three broad roots and a fire flickering inside the trunk. Chalky pipped and scrabbled so excitedly that Hedy had to grasp the little creature and shove it back into her sweater. The naiad pointed west. She was trying to tell them something, and Hedy was sure that, whatever it was, it was about the Spellbound Tree.

Time resumed, and so did the fall of the suspended wave.

When the breakers stopped washing over the bridge, it took some time for the terrified drivers to start their vehicles and begin moving across. By then, the children riding extinct animals through Paris were lost from sight.

Not long after they had crossed the river, Hedy could feel her sivatherium begin to transform. Step by step, it shrank – and she could see the same happening to the animals that the others rode.

There was a sharp whistle from up high somewhere. *Was it Tempest?* she wondered. *Can gargoyles whistle?* The thylacine in particular pricked its ears at the sound, and with a bark turned down a side street to track it down.

Their movements slowed the closer they got to that sporadic whistle. The smaller they grew, the more their scales and fur hardened. The barks and snorts and snaps fell silent. At last, Hedy and the others found their feet touching the ground. With a clatter, their small carousel rides fell to the cobbles.

Tempest landed nearby, panting at the weight she'd been carrying with the faceless grotesque. She wasn't the only one. All of them breathed hard, as though they had been the ones doing the running. Jelly, as wobbly as her nickname, had to put her hand against the wall to keep upright.

'Did you make them turn back?' Hedy asked, waving at the carousel animals.

Jelly shook her head. 'No. Not intentionally anyway.'

Doug wriggled his way out of Spencer's arms and scampered to the piano stool.

'Stan?' He snuffled the fawn's face with his wet bear's nose. 'Wake up.'

'Mmmm, awake,' mumbled the little deer, eyes fluttering. 'I had a dream I was flying.'

*Fweee-whew.* The whistle came from above them. When they looked up, they spotted the giant lips and eye from Violette's edging over the building. The lips had been the mysterious whistler guiding the animals. The large eye swivelled expressively at a roomy door recess in a building nearby. Hedy took the hint and shepherded everyone into the space.

Bunched together, hidden from cursory looks up and down the street, they chattered and nursed Stan, until the lips said, *Shhhhhh*. A minute later, the sound of a police siren sailed across the top of the street and away, accompanied by the hum of a couple of motor scooters. They hadn't been tracked.

Moving like huge, oddly shaped caterpillars, the lips and eye hastened down. As soon as it was within quiet earshot, the lips began gabbling at them.

'Violette has been taken,' they said in accented English. 'Not long after you left, some strangers came into the studio – which is on the other side of this block of buildings – and they questioned Violette. They seemed to know about you children. She wouldn't tell them anything and they covered her mouth with a cloth to make her fall asleep. Then they carried her to a black vehicle with black windows and drove away.'

Hedy's stomach dropped. 'She was taken because of us?'

'*Oui!*'

Max groaned. 'Why do all these grown-ups need saving all the time?'

'Hey, Jelly,' said Spencer, 'can you find where Bess is with your magic?'

Looking entirely spent, Jelly said, 'I don't have a clue how to find things. The only thing I seem to know how to do is move things. Zits from here to there. Us from there to here.' She rubbed a hand over her ashen face. 'And right now, I feel wrung out like Dad's old mop.'

'Well then,' said Tempest, '*I* shall have to find where they are.'

The gargoyle flexed her wings with such confidence that a tiny shard of hope pierced Hedy's despair. 'How?' she asked.

'I shall ask the grotesques of the city to help me. Poor, burnt Notre Dame is not the only edifice in Paris with watchful eyes.'

CHAPTER 15

# THE GHOST AND THE BELLICOSE
# GROTESQUES

Not knowing another safe place to go, they took
the risk of settling in to wait in Violette's apartment. Hedy coaxed Chalky out of her sweater and the
little creature sniffed its way around their group,
getting to know them.

Spencer turned Chalky over gently on his lap. 'It's
a boy.'

Doug and Stan took a closer look and, on seeing it
to be true, fell about in a fit of giggles.

They followed Chalky around the apartment like a

line of ducklings, watching him dart into corners and under tables and chairs. At one point, he got stuck under the couch, and lit up with a powerful red glow until he was freed.

In all the excitement, they'd missed lunch. Spencer and Max poked around inside Violette's fridge, and before long, they were buttering some bread and devouring it with chunks of Brie and some strawberries.

'I wonder if Bess is OK,' said Spencer, feeding Chalky crumbs of bread.

'He will be.' Jelly pulled Doug into her lap and gave him a squeeze. 'We saw him half drowned once and he bounced back from that and chased us over the sea. Didn't we, Doug?'

Doug nodded. 'Uh-huh. He was like this.' The bear cub flopped over her lap in his best impression of a half-drowned treasure hunter, tongue lolling to the side dramatically.

Sundown, when Tempest had said she would return, was hours away so they settled in to wait as patiently as they could.

Hedy and Jelly played with Chalky on the floor, and happened upon a sort of peekaboo game that actually made the little creature laugh. Each time they covered their eyes, tapped their nose and cupped their ears he glowed a bright daffodil yellow and quivered happily. It cheered both of them to see him light up, although Jelly was still feeling out of sorts after her unexpected bout of magic, and soon fell asleep. Chalky tucked himself against her chest and followed suit, looking far from fearsome and dangerous.

As Doug, Stan and Max played an imaginary game together, Hedy and Spencer drifted over to the box in which Violette had kept the Rosetta Jumbler.

'I wonder why Violette hasn't put it away,' Spencer remarked.

Hedy knelt next to her brother as he looked in the box. 'She misses her dad a lot. Maybe she wanted to keep these mementoes of his out for a while. You know, like Mum with those photo albums sometimes.'

'Do you think they're maker things?'

With great care, Spencer began gently lifting things up. There were ordinary-looking items such as a pair of earmuffs, a set of paintbrushes, as well as more mysterious ones. A candle shaped like the letter S with a wick at both ends. A beautiful miniature door (Hedy had seen so many beautiful doors around Paris) carved with twining flowers and the head of a mythical animal. And a small instrument that looked like a cross between a violin and an abacus.

'Hey, look at this!' Spencer said, holding up a tube about the size of a tube of toothpaste. 'I'm sure this is Mrs Pal's handwriting.' A handwritten label on the tube said *Glue*. 'I bet this is some of her special glue. The *glue* glue.'

'Like the kind she gave us to fix Mrs Vilums's broken hand that time?' Hedy recalled.

Spencer nodded. 'Do you think I could use just a little bit?'

'What for?'

He scooted to his bag and untied the collapsed skyskepnur rod that had travelled with them all this way. 'To fix the puncture holes in the water bulb. Nothing I've tried plugs them up, but I reckon *glue* glue would. I should've thought of it before.'

'How can you be thinking of fixing that at a time like this?'

'Mrs Pal told me, always be making,' said Spencer.

Hedy pulled him into a headlock and ruffled his hair. 'She never said any such thing.'

'I'll even buy some more from Mrs Pal and send it to Violette to replace it,' Spencer laughed.

*If we ever see Mrs Pal again*, Hedy thought. But it felt good to hear her brother laugh, so she didn't say it. She didn't know Mrs Pal quite as well as Spencer, but she thought the maker would want him to try to fix his ramshackle, impractical rod. 'Maybe just a tiny bit of glue.'

The last flush of orange was fading from the sky when Tempest arrived.

'We have found them,' she crowed. 'It is not so far from here. The Grutz fellow is there, and four or five others. One of the Paris gargoyles is sure she saw Bess being dragged into the building.'

Tempest described the layout of the building as best she could, and after some time talking over one another, they had a plan.

There was only one major point of contention.

'You're staying, Max,' Jelly said. 'You and the animals.'

Max fumed. 'But I'm the one with the sword!'

'Exactly! You have to stay here and keep it safe, and protect Doug and Stan and Chalky. You're the big brother for them. Lock the door behind us, don't let anyone in.'

'You can't leave us here!' Max insisted. 'What if

other bogs come here and snatch us? They got Violette, and we're all smaller than her.'

There was a rap on the window where the great eye and lips had been eavesdropping.

'He is right,' said the lips. 'You should stay together. Allow me to join you and I will do my best to keep them safe. Close by, but out of danger.'

Out on the street, Tempest flapped from one corner to the next, swiftly shepherding them north-east. She carried the lips, which had curled themselves up as small as they could so that Tempest could transport them. Taking turns carrying Simon's piano stool, they arrived at the cul-de-sac that was their destination less than twenty minutes later, sweaty and out of breath.

Two Paris grotesques – a hook-beaked bird and another that Hedy could only describe as some sort of demon – were on a rooftop nearby, keeping their target under surveillance. After a quick word with them, Tempest flapped down to the street.

'The building we want is that red one,' she said.

In the dim light of the cul-de-sac, Hedy picked out a sign, *Mémoire Magique*.

'They report that no one has come in or out since I

left,' Tempest continued. 'I shall put out the street lights to darken the street more and provide cover. Then we can commence our operation.'

'You're kind of enjoying this, aren't you?' said Hedy.

The gargoyle rolled her wing-joints around, a fighter limbering up. 'It is in my nature to be good at this, if that is what you mean.'

She whistled softly to the lips and they came skimming down the side of the shadowy building. 'Max, Doug and Stan, you must hide in here until we say it is safe to come out.'

The lips opened up wider than they'd seen them stretch before, allowing Max and the two small animals to climb inside.

'It's like being in a sack,' Max told them, peeking over the lower lip. He gently took Chalky from Hedy. 'And I thought there'd be way more spit.'

'It's very dark in here,' Stan mumbled.

As though he understood the fawn, Chalky began to faintly glow inside the dark mouth like a toddler's night light.

With its passengers safe inside, the lips closed up and scrunched and stretched its way upwards to the roof.

'Simon,' said Tempest, 'are you ready?'

Simon's ghostly form coalesced beside them. 'I am ready for my great performance.'

Tempest launched into the air. A moment later, they heard a smash, then another, and another, as she used her claws to punch out the street lamps nearest to the red building.

Stumbling in the dark, Hedy, Spencer and Jelly hurried forwards and placed Simon's piano stool right outside the door of Mémoire Magique.

'Over to you now, Simon,' Hedy whispered. 'Tell them you're coming to get them or something like that.'

'I shall tell them that I will eat their livers for eternity,' he said, 'that their souls will hang in the fires of—'

'You're kind of scaring me but that all sounds good. Just go!'

They couldn't see him in the dark, but the coolness of his presence diminished as he passed through the door. Moments later, they heard a deep spine-chilling croon, followed by harsh threats of all sorts of otherworldly torture that made Spencer curl in against Hedy's side.

'Wow, he's really hamming it up, isn't he?' Jelly said, ear to the door.

There were shouts of fright inside. Furniture

toppled over, crockery shattered on the floor, people swore at the tops of their voices. Time for the next phase of their operation.

'Tempest, go!' Hedy called out.

The gargoyle pitched herself through the top-storey window like a cannonball, her Paris comrades right behind her.

More shocked cries could be heard deeper inside the red building as its occupants found themselves trapped between a ghost and three bellicose grotesques. It took a minute for the door at the front to *click-clack* as Tempest unlocked it.

'Quickly,' she urged them. 'We have herded the enemy to the kitchen, but one of them has a broomstick. I fear he will land a blow on our Notre Dame friends.'

'Where's Bess?' Hedy asked as they trooped inside.

'I haven't seen him yet. But there are many things in which they could be hiding him.'

Tempest's meaning soon became clear. The place was stuffed full of stage show magic paraphernalia. On the wall there were paintings of illusionists mid-performance; glass cabinets were crammed with toys and props; there were trick mirrors and false torsos and rigged boxes.

'Looks like Uncle John decided to set up a creepy second home in Paris,' Jelly joked uneasily.

Spencer looked at her darkly. 'This place is nothing like Hoarder Hill.'

'If you say so.'

At that moment, Simon's head appeared through the wall, startling a squeak from Spencer. 'I have found Bess,' he said. 'And Violette also!'

He guided them into a room a couple of doorways along. Leaning against the wall were two boxes painted to look like Egyptian sarcophagi.

'Are they magic boxes?' Spencer asked Jelly.

'Um. Why are you asking me?'

'Can't you sense magic or anything like that?'

Jelly held her hand out towards the sarcophagi and then wiggled her fingers. 'I have zero idea of what I'm supposed to do here.'

A muffled groan leaked from one of the boxes. Hedy gingerly opened the front panel. It was empty. She patted down the sides until her fingers located a small pull and when she tugged on it, the false back panel lifted. Behind it was a groggy Bess, barely able to open his eyes.

Spencer hurriedly did the same to the other

sarcophagus and found Violette hidden inside. She was still asleep.

Towards the back of the building there was a crash and a thump, followed by a mighty screech of rage.

'We have to get out of here,' Hedy said, helping Bess out of the disappearing box.

But the treasure hunter had no more strength than a newborn kitten. Hedy had to prop him up. It was left to Spencer and Jelly to bring Violette and they found that for a slim woman, she was a heavy bundle of limbs to drag between them. They were still metres away from the front door when Tempest shot from the kitchen, screaming for them to hurry. Mr Grutz lumbered in her wake, stoop-shouldered and furious, a broom handle in one hand and a kettle in the other.

'Stop right there,' he shouted.

'Stay away from us,' Hedy shot back as they made it through the door. 'Or we'll stuff you into a trick box so far you'll never get out. We know what you are. We know you're trying to kill off magic.'

Mr Grutz's look of shock told Hedy she'd gotten it wrong, even before he spoke. 'You idiots,' he grated. 'Someone is trying to kill off the Spellbound Tree and magic, but it's not me.'

## CHAPTER 16

### STALEMATE

Hedy froze in her tracks. If it wasn't Mr Grutz and his band of bogs trying to harm the Spellbound Tree, who was it?

Grutz waved a tired hand. 'Come inside and I'll tell you what we know. The Paris police are looking for the whole damn lot of us after the chaos you caused on the streets today.'

Bess was as floppy as a rag doll against her and Violette still hadn't woken up. They weren't going to make it anywhere fast. Hedy was not, however, about to go further into the bogs' lair. 'We can hear you fine from here. What do you know?'

'We know there's a rogue operator out there who's a bunny short of a magician's hat,' said Mr Grutz. 'A double-crossing magician, trying to do away with magic. The Spellbound Tree is already waning but they're out to destroy it altogether, before anyone else can revive it. We were tipped off yesterday when an alarm went off. It told us some big magic trouble had happened around your grandparents' house. That's why some of my colleagues think that double-crossing magician is none other than your grandfather.'

'That's ridiculous!' Spencer sputtered. 'Why would Grandpa John want to hurt the Spellbound Tree and magic?'

'It's logical if you think about it. He doesn't trust it,' said Mr Grutz. 'Not after your grandmother went missing for so long. So he hates it. Wants to see it wiped out.'

'That's not true,' said Spencer. 'Not any more. Right, Hedy?'

She avoided Spencer's eyes. Perhaps Grandpa John had stopped distrusting magic for a time, after they had saved Grandma Rose. But recently, a fear of magic had returned. Even so, she didn't think that his fear had transformed into hatred and a desire to kill off magic. Certainly he wouldn't have done it if he'd known the rest of their family would disappear too.

'I reached out a hand to help him,' Mr Grutz continued. 'He wouldn't have a thing to do with me.'

'It's no accident you moved into the house next door to him, is it?' Jelly asked.

Mr Grutz screwed up his nose as though there was an unpleasant smell. 'We thought your grandfather needed watchful eyes kept on him.'

'If you're one of those bogs policing magic, why would you care?' said Hedy. 'You guys *want* magic to be killed off.'

'Because your grandfather, or whoever is behind all this, doesn't give a damn what else they kill off with it. We may not like it, but magic has seeped into the fibre of many of the people, places and things we hold dear. The disintegration has already started.'

'Like the British Museum,' said Spencer.

'Exactly. If it were just the world of magicians eating itself, I'd sit back with a box of popcorn. But if it affects all of us . . . that's a different story. Like it or not, and I don't, our fates are all connected.'

'Whoever is trying to hurt magic, it's not Grandpa

John,' said Hedy firmly. 'He was going to save it. We found his notes.'

To her surprise, Mr Grutz actually looked relieved. But he swiftly masked it, narrowing his eyes. 'Then where is he? Wouldn't the Amazing John Sang at least come himself to save his *treasure hunter* here?'

Bess stood a little straighter next to Hedy, but all he managed in reply was a scathing look at Mr Grutz.

'You're a creep, stuffing people into coffins,' Spencer muttered.

'They were only trick boxes, for heaven's sake, not real sarcophagi. And I did think this sneaky thief was working for the man trying to kill off magic. So where's John hiding?'

'Do you really think he'd send us if he could come himself?' said Hedy. 'He's been trapped by whatever is going on!'

'Trapped where?'

Hedy clamped her mouth shut, and silenced Spencer and Jelly with a look. She didn't have much faith in Mr Grutz's intentions for Grandpa John.

'I didn't see him at the house,' Mr Grutz continued.

'You call Bess a sneaky thief when *you're* the one breaking into people's homes?' Jelly exploded.

But he ignored her, piecing together a theory. 'I think whatever has happened to him, you brought him along, and you have him here in Paris.' When none of them refuted him, he knew he'd struck the truth. 'Tell you what. If you bring us your grandfather, we'll bring you a magician to fix him. We've got one off the books, so to speak. But there's a condition.'

Hedy felt Bess squeeze her shoulder warningly. 'What's that?' she asked suspiciously.

'You hand over that thing you brought out of the Dodo Manège.' Mr Grutz squared his hunched shoulders. 'See, there are two things we need to get this sorted out. You have the chalkydri, but *we* have the crucial piece to open the way to the Spellbound Tree. Can't rely on these magicians to get it fixed. The fools can't even defend themselves against getting trapped in jewels and scrolls and whatnot. So it'll have to be us who gets this done.'

With Tempest and her grotesque friends keeping a surly watch over the bogs, Hedy and the others huddled together to decide what to do. Having Grandpa John freed was exactly what they wanted of course, but to give Chalky over to the bogs? Hedy would have loved someone to take the responsibility for saving magic from them, but handing the baton to Mr Grutz felt like letting the fox into the henhouse.

'I don't think we have much of a choice,' said Bess.

'But you're still half knocked out,' Jelly pointed out. Although Bess was now standing on his own without help, he did look a bit pasty-faced.

Simon's face appeared hazily near them. 'I do not trust that Grutz will not chop up my piano stool for kindling and cast me into the unknown.'

Hedy sighed. 'Bess is right though. Unless any of us have a bright idea, the best thing we can do is get Grandpa John out of that snow globe.'

'And Lark,' Spencer added.

'And Lark, of course,' Hedy agreed. 'Maybe Grandpa John can convince Greedy Grutz to let him do what needs doing.'

With Mr Grutz and one of his henchmen watching, they called the lips down from the roof. It was rather enjoyable to watch the pair of bogs go slack-jawed at the sight of Max and the animals clambering out of the great mouth. A tell-tale orange glow and twittering from Max's wild thatch of hair gave Chalky away, even though he seemed to be trying to hide.

'Hand the thing over,' Mr Grutz said.

Hedy moved in between Max and the bogs. 'No. You get our grandfather free first and then . . . then we'll join forces.'

The henchman sniggered. 'You don't have a strong hand to play here, young lady.'

Crossing her arms, Hedy said, 'Our ghost could put a chill in you so terrible that you'd lose your face to frostbite in five minutes flat. And our friendly giant lips could swallow you both right now, and no one would ever hear from you again.'

They could have heard a pin drop in the alley. Finally, Mr Grutz barked in laughter. 'All right. Let's see this grandfather of yours.'

Hedy gently pulled the snow globes from their towel wadding in the bag. Mr Grutz took a long look at Grandpa John, and then squinted at the tiny figure in the other snow globe. 'Is that the nurse?'

'Yes. Her name's Lark.'

'Magician?'

Hedy shook her head.

'Poor thing, getting caught up in all this mess. Well, we'll see if we can get her out first. I'll make a call now.'

*

– 164 –

Mr Grutz's mysterious 'off the books' magician was a man introduced as Smithy, although Hedy suspected that wasn't his real name. He looked like he'd been hiding in an attic for a month. He was bug-eyed and fidgety, and even from here Hedy could see that his shoulders were lightly dusted with dandruff.

'Who's this lot?' Smithy asked Mr Grutz, waving a finger at Hedy and the others. His voice was rather nasal.

'We've struck a deal with them,' said Mr Grutz. 'They have something we need. You have our permission to help them with their predicament.' He held up Grandpa John's snow globe that he'd forced Hedy to hand over.

Smithy's eyes bulged even more as he took in the figure sleeping within the glass. 'Who the heck is that?'

'This is John Sang.'

'The Amazing John Sang?'

'That's right.'

Smithy whistled. 'That's an old-school name in magician circles. Who's that in the other one?'

'His home nurse, she's collateral damage. Free her first, then him. I need John Sang in one piece. There's information we need out of him. How long will it take?'

Smithy grimaced. 'An hour. More or less.'

'Make it less. I'm pretty sure the authorities are looking for us after all that mess on the bridge. We don't want to stay here too much longer. If they connect our vehicles to this address it won't be a safe house soon.' He shivered. 'I'm going to have a cuppa to warm myself up. I'll want to see some progress when I get back.'

Hedy had thought that perhaps they'd feel a sense of kinship with the magician, but for all his prattle, Smithy seemed like a cagey sort of fellow. His eyes flitted over them like a fly, before settling on Max. 'So, this kid with the metal glove. Is that another thing I'm supposed to undo? Don't see why they need me when there's perfectly good meat cleavers around.' At their darkening faces, he let out a laugh. 'Come on, that was a joke. No one wants to clean up that amount of blood. So, who *are* you lot?'

There was an awkward silence until Spencer, irked, said, 'We're the Hoarder Hill Four.'

Smithy didn't try too hard to stifle his laughter. 'The Hoarder Hill Four. Got badges, have you? Secret handshake? By the way, there are more than four of you. Maths not your strong point then?'

Smithy had arrived with a suitcase – the only well-kept thing about him – and after turning each of the snow globes over to inspect them, he opened up the suitcase and began to paw through it.

Spencer was the most curious, of course, but Hedy, Jelly and Max shuffled to get a closer look too. All sorts of odd items were inside, many that would look entirely at home in Mrs Pal's workshop at the Palisade. A few books, engraved tins, handles orphaned from whatever they were supposed to open or carry, and a lot of other things tucked into felt compartments. There was even a china plate broken in two pieces.

'Oi, out of there,' Smithy said to Doug and Stan, who had scampered over to nose at the suitcase. But for the first time, he spoke without that heckling edge to his voice, and he gently pulled the animals to either side of him, giving them each a rub on their head. Hedy warmed to him ever so slightly.

'I thought all magicians in this part of the world were turned into sleeping beauties,' said Bess. 'How did you escape?'

'Whoever did this doesn't know about me, that's

why,' Smithy replied, picking at the artefacts he'd brought along. 'I'm off the grid. Avoid gatherings like the plague. The Fantastikhana, the conclave, Rabble's annual barbecue. Any guest list that the Sleight might keep and monitor, I ain't on.'

'Why?' Jelly asked.

He gestured at the snow globes lined up on the floor. 'That's what happens when you're on a list. A misfit with a vendetta catches you in a Morpheus Web.' At their blank looks, Smithy added, 'You never heard of a Morpheus Web? That's what she set off to trap everyone.'

**CHAPTER 17**

## ROCK, PAPER, SCISSORS

'She?' Hedy startled. 'The rogue magician is a she?'

Smithy nodded, smug at having some gossip.

'Who is it?' Bess asked.

'Don't know who. But rumour is that it's someone who used to be a big talent. A lot of power, a lot of promise. But just like Icarus, she flew too close to the sun. Tried a magic so potent it backfired. Now she has nothing left.'

'How do people know all of this but not know her identity?' Jelly asked, incredulous.

'Magicians brag on anonymous webchats just like bogs do. She went by the username "Rowanberry". The theory goes, she's so gutted at losing her magic ability, she wants to burn down the whole toy store so that no one else can play either.'

'If she doesn't have any magic,' said Spencer, 'how could she subdue all the magicians of the UK and France?'

Smithy tsked. 'Just like you can throw a grenade into a trench without much training, you can set off a magical device without being able to control magic. All she would've needed was a maker without much in way of morals. And there are a few of those lying around in the rattier corners of the globe.'

Spencer pointed at the contents of Smithy's suitcase. 'Did you make these?' With a look at the china plate halves, he added, 'Or break them?'

'Hardly. I'm like most magicians. We let makers do the making.'

Smithy decided on three things from his suitcase: a pair of scissors shaped like a stork, a scroll, and a stone. Flexing his fingers, he said, 'My old reliables.'

'Are they made to undo Morpheus Webs?' Spencer asked.

'Nothing's *made* to do that,' scoffed Smithy. 'I'm improvising. Scissors to cut the web of the spell. Write the restoring enchantment on the scroll of P—' He caught himself, as though remembering there were secrets he wanted to keep. 'The scroll of parchment. And the stone to break the glass.'

Hedy snatched up the snow globes, panicked. 'Can't you magic the glass away?'

'Sorry, I didn't bring my magic glass-dissolving underpants,' said Smithy sarcastically. 'Settle down, I'll break it gently. Besides, a trinity works best. Three things together, you know?'

'Why three things?' Spencer asked. Despite the circumstances, he was soaking up every scrap of learning he could.

'Because triangles are the strongest shape.' Smithy suddenly smirked, nodding his head at the scroll, scissors and stone in front of him. 'Ha! It's Rock, Paper, Scissors!'

Hedy groaned. '*This* is how you're saving magic? A kids' game?'

'Yes, a kids' game. The best magic I've done came out of playing and daydreaming. Geez, who died and sucked all the fun out of your life?'

*Snip, snip, snip.* Hedy couldn't detect what Smithy was trimming away. It seemed the magician was cautiously clipping the empty air around Lark's snow globe, about a centimetre away from the surface. He'd been at it for half an hour. Violette had woken up and both she and Bess were reviving with a strong cup of tea that the bogs brought them. Mr Grutz stuck his head in regularly to check on Smithy's progress, steadily growing just as impatient as Hedy.

'Is it an actual invisible web you're cutting?' Spencer asked eventually.

'Sort of,' said Smithy. 'There are strands of the spell all around this sucker. Don't you sense them?'

Spencer shook his head. He turned to Jelly. 'Can you?'

Jelly reached a hand towards the snow globe. 'I can't tell if I'm feeling anything. I don't think I am.'

'Oh, are you the magician in this bunch?' Smithy jabbed the scissors in Hedy's direction. 'I thought it was the boss lady here. Well, if you close your eyes, that'll help.'

Jelly closed her eyes.

'Now, you're trying to feel with your fingers and the

centre of your chest at the same time. It's kind of like heartburn. This spot right between the lungs, near the spine. You're trying to push out and be aware with that and . . . and that whole awareness links up with your hands.'

He went back to his snipping, as everyone else watched Jelly. Suddenly her eyes popped open. 'I think I felt it. I felt the heartburn.'

'Not fair! I want to feel heartburn too,' said Max, dropping to his knees beside her.

As though she'd had it mastered for years, Jelly began telling Max what to do, and with paw and hoof thrust out, Doug and Stan tried to copy him.

Without drawing attention to herself, Hedy closed her eyes and listened, trying to sense that unfamiliar awareness between her lungs, near the spine. Suddenly, an image appeared in her mind. Through a thatch of dark hair, she saw herself, cross-legged on the floor in this very room, eyes closed. It wasn't only an image – she felt warm, cosy, hidden – and she could hear Smithy's voice, although it was a meaningless murmur from this perspective.

Hedy's eyes popped open. She gaped at the top of Max's head, where Chalky's snout poked through his hair, bright eyes looking at her curiously. *Did I just mind-meld with Chalky?* she thought. She was too stunned to really register Smithy's relieved mumble that he was nearly done.

*Wham!* A thrumming filled her ears. Hedy felt like she was being whipped around the inside of a tornado. *This is not heartburn!* Somewhere through the noise, she heard the incomprehensible yell of a man, 'No, don't, let me—' And then it was gone.

Opening her eyes, everything was a blur. The thrumming had stopped, and she was lying on the floor. Looking carefully to the left and right, Hedy found everyone else had toppled over too.

'What just happened?' she mumbled. Sitting up made her dizzy, but she did it anyway.

On the other side of the room, a soaking wet figure pushed herself up to a seated position. Brown bobbed hair hung in dripping strands around a pixie-like face. Lark had been freed from the snow globe.

'Lark!' Hedy cried. She crawled on hands and knees to join her.

'Where is this?' said Lark, and then she winced in pain. 'Ouch, my head!'

'You're in Paris. With me, Spencer, Jelly and Max.

And some of our friends.'

'How did I get to Paris? Where's John?'

Hedy swung around to look for her grandfather. Doug had already recovered and was using his wet nose to rouse the others. But Grandpa John wasn't amongst them. Instead, she spotted his snow globe still intact, white flakes dancing around his miniature form. Smithy hadn't gotten him out yet.

Mr Grutz stumbled into the room, looking as though he'd only just struggled to his feet too. He was clutching a small metal tube. 'What on earth did you do? Where's Smithy?'

Doug looked up from where he was sniffing the magician's suitcase. 'He's here!'

The bear cub nosed at the china plate broken into two pieces. Instead of the faded floral pattern, the plate now captured the likeness of Smithy.

Jelly immediately put her palms up. 'My heartburn did *not* do that. At least, I don't think it did. And if I did, I definitely didn't mean to.'

'My guess is the Morpheus Web was somehow rigged to turn on someone trying to undo it,' said Bess, crouching over Smithy's broken plate.

'P-pardon me,' Lark stammered, 'but what on earth

are you talking about?'

They tried to break the news gently to her, but it was a lot for anyone to take in all at once: magic and magicians, she and Grandpa John trapped in snow globes, their family vanishing, their quest through Paris. Lark stared at the peculiar Mémoire Magique artefacts around them, either strangely composed or numb from shock, saying very little.

'How are we going to free Grandpa John now?' asked Spencer.

Mr Grutz shook his head at the tube in his hand. 'Well, we can't stay here to figure it out. The coppers are on their way. I knew we should have switched those number plates on the motor scooters! No more playing around, now, you have to hand over that chalkydri.'

As though Mr Grutz had tapped a vein of summoning magic in himself, a team of French police burst into the Mémoire Magique at that precise moment.

It was chaos. The police had arrived probably expecting Mr Grutz and a handful of bogs. Instead their foray was complicated by an unexpected group of youngsters, three other strangers and some small animals.

People ran to and fro, punches were thrown and

Hedy found herself backed into a corner with Spencer, Jelly, Max and Lark, the animals in their arms. Mr Grutz and Bess were forced to lie face down on the floor in handcuffs and when Violette tried to explain things to the police, her outraged tone only served to have her handcuffed and forced to the floor as well.

'Will they let us go?' Spencer whispered. 'We're only kids.'

But a senior officer strode into the room, scrutinizing their faces and checking some printed pictures in her hand. The pictures appeared to have been taken from video footage – they were grainy but good enough. Shots of the bogs' van and their motor scooters, but also pictures of the children riding extinct animals through the gates of the Jardin des Plantes.

'I think we're nicked too,' groaned Jelly.

As the police conferred in the corridor, Mr Grutz hissed, 'Oi, kids, you have to get out of here.' He jerked his head at the tube, which had dropped to the floor in the commotion and rolled under a cabinet. 'Grab that. Do *not* lose it. Get to the Richelieu Library at eight tomorrow morning. Ask for Fossile. She's one of the librarians there. She's the one you need to open the gate to the Spellbound Tree.'

*I know where to find the ancient one.* The note that Mr Grutz had handed to Hedy, that she'd never had a chance to give to Grandpa John, and which was scrunched in her pocket still; now its meaning became clear. Fossile.

'We can't leave you here,' Hedy whispered, mostly talking to Bess and Violette.

'You must,' said Bess firmly. 'Getting out of this pickle will take time that the Spellbound Tree might not have, that your grandfather and your family might not have.'

'Jelly, can you transfer us out of this place? Outside, where we can make a run for it?' Max asked.

Jelly screwed up her face and they all held their breath for a few moments. But she opened her eyes and sighed. 'I don't know what to do.'

'If only Tempest could blind them so we could get away,' Spencer muttered.

'Blind them?' asked Stan, shocked.

'Only for a short time. Gently.'

The police finished conferring amongst themselves and came back into the room, looking for all the world like a long interrogation was about to begin.

Suddenly, an intense beam of light shot out of the

top of Max's head, shining straight at the hapless police, making them cry out in pain.

'It's Chalky!' Hedy cried. She lunged forwards and grabbed Mr Grutz's metal tube. 'Run!'

They scrambled to their feet and darted to the doorway. Bess and Violette were struggling to roll over and get to their feet, but the police, eyes smarting, fell on to the pair, accidentally cutting off their escape.

At the shouting, some other police came running from the kitchen where they'd been guarding Mr Grutz's henchmen. But they had not counted on screeching grotesques scratching at them with stone claws, nor a ghost materializing from the walls, snarling dreadful threats of pain and terror. With their friends shielding them from chase, Hedy and the others ran into the night.

## CHAPTER 18

### FOSSILE

They ran until they reached busier streets where moving slower would attract less notice. People were dining, drinking, strolling and carrying on with all the ordinary, pleasant things that one could do in Paris if unburdened by the fate of a magical tree. No one stopped them as they gradually made their way to the banks of the Seine.

A cobblestone walkway lined the river, below street level so they felt slightly more hidden. Without a destination, they walked along until they found themselves at the bridge where they'd caused such a scene earlier that day.

Something swooped, but it was only Tempest. She and her grotesque friends deposited Simon's piano stool at their feet.

'What happened to Bess and Violette and Mr Grutz?' Hedy asked.

'All under arrest,' Tempest replied. 'The police are not chasing you – they are still gathering their wits. But you should try to keep out of sight. Here under Pont Neuf will do.' She turned to the Paris grotesques and said a few words of thanks. With friendly grunts, the grotesques flew off in the direction of Notre Dame.

They clustered under the archway of the bridge, exhausted. No Bess, no Violette, no money between them, but at least they had Grandpa John's snow globe and – in an unexpected turn of events – they had Lark.

'Are you OK?' Hedy asked her.

Lark's eyes fell on Tempest and Simon. 'I feel like I'm in a dream still. But otherwise I'm OK, thank you. What do we do now? Find this Fossile person at the library?'

Hedy nodded. 'And we take this to her.' She gingerly unscrewed the small cap from Mr Grutz's metal tube, half afraid that it would set off a magical booby trap like the one that had caught Smithy. But there was no eruption. Inside it was a single sheet of paper. Hedy eased the paper out. It had been torn from a book, but it was completely blank.

Lark held out her hand tentatively to have a closer look. The page trembled in her fingers.

'You're shivering,' Jelly said sympathetically. 'You must be in shock.'

'Wet and cold, that's all,' Lark assured her. She studied the paper closely. 'What's it supposed to say?'

'None of us know.' Hedy sighed. 'We never have the full story for any of this stuff.'

Chalky pipped and scampered down Max's shoulder, intrigued by the torn piece of paper.

'What do you know about this, Chalky?' Spencer asked, picking the creature up and holding him close to the page.

As Chalky sniffed and tilted his head at it inquisitively, he began to pulse a deep shade of sapphire blue.

'What do you think blue means?' said Jelly. When she got a blank look from everyone she groaned. 'Come on, don't you think he's like a mood ring? Changes colour depending on what he's feeling?'

Lark made cooing noises at Chalky and held out her arm for him to climb on to. But he was more interested in leaping from Spencer's hands to Max's hair and playing hide and seek.

Hedy took the page back and placed it safely in the metal tube. 'Lark, what happened to you at Grandpa John's?'

Lark stared at the river, thinking back. 'I'd . . . I'd just finished taking his blood pressure when he suddenly ran away, shouting. It was very odd. I ran after him, to his study. Only just got to the doorway when something happened. It was like being hit by a ten-metre wave. The next thing I knew, I woke up in that strange room with you all.'

'What was it like in the snow globe?' Spencer asked.

She crossed her arms with another shiver. 'Like sleeping. Have you ever been dreaming, and you knew you were dreaming, but you couldn't make yourself wake up?' Shaking off the memory, Lark tilted her head at Max's gauntlet. 'Do you want help getting that off?'

'You can *try*,' said Max. 'But we haven't been able to budge it.'

'Maybe a nurse can manage it.'

Jelly snorted dubiously. 'If you get that thing off his

arm, you wouldn't be a nurse, you'd be a magician.'

Lark pulled and prodded and wiggled the gauntlet, but didn't have any more luck than the rest of them.

They stopped talking as a couple of people approached, enjoying a night-time stroll along the river. Doug and Stan wedged themselves under Simon's piano stool as best they could, with Spencer sitting on it to hide them from sight with his legs. The strangers caught sight of Lark with her wet hair and clothes and the woman asked something in French, concerned.

'They ask if Lark is all right,' Simon whispered, invisible behind them.

'Oh, *oui*, *oui*!' Lark exclaimed. She pointed at herself, then the river, and pantomimed falling into the water.

It satisfied the couple. They chuckled and kept walking.

'That was smooth, Lark,' Jelly said admiringly. 'I thought *I* was good at cover stories.'

'Do you think someone's going to call the police?' said Spencer. 'You know, a good Samaritan worried about a group of kids sleeping on the ground under a bridge?'

They all agreed the police probably had Violette's address by now, so they couldn't wait out the night there, and none of them remembered the address of the bakery where they'd exited the Paris slip. Their entire group was bone-tired too; they couldn't walk all night.

'Sleep,' said Tempest. 'I shall keep watch from atop the bridge, and scare off anyone who advances towards your position.'

'Thanks, Tempest,' said Hedy. 'We just have to make it to morning, and then head to the library to find Fossile.'

Unsurprisingly, cobblestones turned out to be a hard and cold bed, but they were too tired to care. Their conversation slowed down, and one by one they fell asleep.

Hedy was woken by a wave of water that slapped loudly on the bank. It had created enough splash to wet her right foot. She sat up, grumbling softly. Lark was sitting nearby, with the metal tube in hand.

'Are you all right?' Hedy asked.

'I've slept enough for a while,' Lark whispered back. She wiggled the tube. 'I was just looking to see if anything had turned up on the page.'

'Has it?'

Lark shook her head.

With a yawn, Hedy said, 'I guess I should keep that safe in my bag. Disaster if we lose it now.' She took it back from Lark and slipped it into her backpack.

'Try to go back to sleep,' said Lark. 'I'll keep watch with the gargoyle.'

'There's something I bet you never thought you'd say.'

Lark smiled. 'Turns out Paris is a magical place.'

*It sure is*, Hedy thought, closing her eyes. As sleep overtook her, she remembered the stone faces decorating the bridge, and how they'd sung for them earlier that day, like they had been raising the river spirit. Magic was in the very bones of the city. Maybe this bridge would also disappear if they didn't save magic.

Wondering where the British Museum and her family had disappeared to, Hedy fell asleep. Her dream was a good one. Mum and Dad were safe and well, Grandpa John and Grandma Rose too, and they were taking care of everything.

*

Tempest woke them the next morning, clutching a large paper bag.

'One of the Notre Dame grotesques gathered this for you,' she explained as they tore open the bag to the buttery smell of croissants.

'They're still warm!' said Spencer around a blissful bite.

'Tempest, what do you mean the grotesque "gathered" them?' asked Hedy.

The gargoyle gave a little shrug. 'She swooped a man who had just bought some breakfast. Now, don't protest. I'm sure if that man knew the importance of your mission, he would have gladly donated them to the cause. Look, Chalky has no qualms about eating the proceeds of crime.'

Chalky was indeed enthusiastically nibbling morsels of croissant that Lark held out in her fingers.

'Nice try,' Hedy smiled, 'he's too little to know any better.'

She bit into the flaky pastry and decided she was too hungry – and the croissant far too delicious – to be high-minded. As she watched Chalky scurry about to find fallen crumbs of pastry, her mind drifted back to the Mémoire Magique, and the moment before

Smithy had freed Lark. Had she only imagined what Chalky was feeling, hidden in Max's hair?

'Should we get going?' said Lark, interrupting her thoughts. 'We don't want to be late to meet this Fossile person.'

The Richelieu Library was nothing like the library at school, or the one near Hedy's home. It was grand and imposing, with sandstone walls and huge, dark metal doors with the words 'Bibliothèque Nationale' above them. A decorative sculpture added to the imposing entrance: a woman's head with ringlets curling either side of her face, as impassive as a sphinx.

'It looks like a really fancy prison, not a library,' said Max, awed.

No one was waiting for them.

'What do we do?' Jelly muttered. 'Knock?'

Feeling a bit foolish, Hedy knocked on the doors. It earned a quizzical look from a passer-by and his small dog but once they were out of earshot, there was a whisper from above.

'*Oui?*'

They looked up. The sculpted woman's face had shifted to regard them.

'Um. Fossile?' Hedy tried.

The sculpture stared, unblinking.

'Simon, can you explain to her we're here to see Fossile?'

The ghostly shimmer in the air floated upwards, level with the sculpture, and he spoke to her in rapid-fire French. At last, she replied with a single word.

Simon floated back down. 'I did what I could.'

'What did she say?'

'To wait.'

Some minutes later, a smaller entrance to the side of the large double doors opened. Out looked an elderly woman with short white hair, bright-red lipstick and a remarkable pair of glasses that looked like daisies. Her expression tensed when she saw them. They were not who she was expecting.

'*Bonjour*, Madame Fossile?' said Hedy.

The woman took half a step backwards. 'Yes?'

'We're here to meet you. Mr Grutz sent us.' Hedy lowered her voice. 'It's about the Spellbound Tree.'

Fossile pursed her lips. 'Come through. These are not things to speak of on the street.'

They filed through the entrance into a courtyard bordered by the sandstone buildings that made up the library. Once there, Doug and Stan strained to be let loose. They'd walked all the way from the bridge, clumsily disguised as dressed dogs hidden under carefully tied sweatshirts and leashed by the troll's whisker. Fossile took in the appearance of a bear cub and fawn with nothing more than a raised eyebrow.

She halted in front of the doors to the foyer. To either side were tall arched windows and atop each one was a decorative face carved in stone.

'Hello,' Doug said, looking up at the window tops.

'Who are you saying hello to?' asked Stan.

'Those people,' Doug replied, peering at the carved faces.

'They're not real people,' scoffed Stan.

'But they're still watching us. Like the lady's face outside.'

Hedy couldn't fault Doug's reasoning. She was beginning to think that every ornamental face in the entire city of Paris was observing what went on, and that they'd been doing it for centuries.

Tempest chose that moment to land in the courtyard. She bobbed her head respectfully at Fossile, who nodded back.

'You say Monsieur Grutz sent you,' Fossile began.

'Why is he not here?'

'He was arrested last night—' Hedy began.

'But,' Jelly interrupted, 'we were working together. It pretty much wasn't our fault.'

'Who are you?' Fossile asked.

Before Spencer could launch into his Hoarder Hill Four prattle again, Hedy said, 'We're the family of John Sang.'

'John Sang the magician?'

'That's right. He's trapped. Nearly every magician in the UK and France is trapped.' Hedy reached into her bag for Grandpa John's snow globe.

'Are you a magician?' Spencer asked. 'Or a maker?'

'No,' said Fossile. 'But someone close to me was.' She bent to look at the snow globe in Hedy's hand and tutted in dismay.

To their shock, the stone faces over the arched windows began to call out questions in hushed French. Fossile, however, was not surprised at all. Over her shoulder, she explained to the faces what she could see.

'I was right!' Doug crowed. 'They are like people!'

'Do you know why Monsieur Grutz sent you here?' Fossile asked.

Hedy pulled out Mr Grutz's metal tube and opened

it to show Fossile the blank piece of paper inside. 'He said to bring you this.'

Fossile froze, except for her eyes which blinked disbelievingly behind her daisy-frame glasses.

Hedy knew that people did not react that way to things they didn't recognize. Hope rising, she said, 'You know what it belongs to?'

A tiny nod. 'My Ines warned this day might come,' said Fossile. 'I was beginning to think I would pass on before it did.'

'Who is . . . Ines?' Hedy asked.

'Ines Impossible. A magician. We were together twenty-seven years. And this page belongs to a book that she bequeathed to the library. The Ember Book.'

## CHAPTER 19

## THE EMBER BOOK

After hearing the short version of their time in Paris, Fossile conferred with the decorative stone faces above the arched windows and came to a decision. She led them inside, through the foyer, and into one of the most magnificent spaces Hedy had ever seen.

Pillars like slender silver birches rose to hold up the ceiling of domes soaring above them. Round windows at the centre of each dome helped to illuminate the massive space. There were bookshelves along the walls, but the room was mostly taken up with rows and rows of desks for quiet reading and research, dotted with lamps that looked like pale-blue mushrooms.

Hushed, as though speaking in a church or a temple, Fossile explained that this was a reading room of the library.

'I hope you know where the Ember Book is,' said Spencer, gawking at the reading room. 'There must be a zillion books in a national library.'

'I do,' Fossile nodded. 'It was hidden here amongst other books, a little like hiding a needle in a haystack. But I always know where it is, even though its hiding spot cannot be simply stumbled upon. Wait here. I won't be long.'

As the library was not yet open, they let Doug and Stan down. The pair scampered through the rows of desks and chairs, pouncing on each other in a roaming game of catch and release.

'No biteys!' Doug yelped, prompting a nervous shush from everyone.

'Your bum is on my face!' Stan complained, rather muffled thanks to the bear bottom sitting on his head.

Spencer chuckled. 'At least it's not *stuck* there like before.'

Chalky leapt excitedly from Max's head into the midst of Doug and Stan's rumble, gently nipping both of them where they were most ticklish. While they played, Hedy stared at the treescapes painted in the great arches of the walls. She felt transported.

Lark took a deep breath by Hedy's side. 'How beautiful,' she said quietly. 'It's so easy to imagine that it's right there.'

'A forest?'

'Yes,' said Lark, wonder in her eyes. 'A tranquil forest, right there.'

When Fossile returned, she was holding a thin leather-bound book. Hedy's heart skipped. It was covered in green leather that was embossed with a design of a tree with three broad roots. Within the tree's trunk outline were the shapes of flames.

'That looks the same as the tree that the river lady made out of water,' said Spencer.

Hedy offered the page to Fossile, but she seemed reluctant to take it. 'What's wrong, madame? Do you know what to do with it?'

'I must replace the page in Ines's book,' said Fossile. 'But if I do, I believe it will call her back. For a short time.'

Hedy looked around them, as though Ines Impossible might be visible already, like an impatient performer waiting in the wings. 'Is that a good thing?'

Fossile sniffed. 'She will not recognize me, I am so old.'

Jelly tutted. 'You're not old, madame. I mean, I don't know your age but I've never seen anyone rock lipstick like you do.'

'Well, perhaps the lipstick *will* tell her who I am.' Fossile allowed herself a very small, self-deprecating smile. But it was short-lived and tears sprang to her eyes. 'If she returns, I will have to say goodbye to her again.'

Not even Jelly had a glib answer to that.

It was Lark who put her arm around Fossile's shoulder comfortingly. 'I'm sure your Ines gave you this responsibility because she believed you would see it through.'

Jelly dug a tissue from her pocket. 'Here, Madame Fossile, I promise I haven't used this tissue. Much.'

After blowing her nose, Fossile adjusted her glasses and opened the book. The leather spine creaked and she turned the pages carefully, as protective as a mother looking at her newborn's fingers for the first time. Less than twenty pages in, she reached a margin of paper torn along its outer edge, the place where a page was missing. Fossile took the sheet of paper from Hedy and slid it into place, holding its curling edges down.

There was a whisper of sound in the quiet of the library. It was far away, many things layered upon one another, perhaps waves breaking on to a sloping shore or an auditorium filled with a hundred clapping hands.

The sudden chill in the air was, literally, a dead give-away. It told Hedy that a ghost had arrived in the room. Behind Fossile, a tall figure materialized, gossamer-like – a woman wearing a black top hat, a tailcoat and bow tie. She had enormous brown eyes that Hedy thought would be warm and friendly under other circumstances. Those eyes swiftly surveyed their whole group, dwelling for a second longer on Max's gauntlet, before settling on Fossile. She whispered something. Fossile stiffened and, without allowing herself to look behind, croakily replied. Hedy didn't understand their words, but the exchange was hesitant, probing and familiar all at once.

'Ines,' said Fossile hoarsely, switching to English, 'these British children are the ones who brought the page here.'

The ghost of Ines Impossible, the late *magicienne*, glided closer. 'Why?' she asked of them. 'Why do you awaken the Ember Book?'

'We need to save the Spellbound Tree,' said Hedy simply. Given the cover of the book, Ines surely knew what she was talking about.

'You?'

Spencer cleared his throat and said nervously, 'We are the Hoarder Hill Four.'

Hedy buried her face in her hands, mortified.

'And what is that?' Ines asked, mouth twitching.

'W-well. I'm a maker,' said Spencer. 'That's Jelly, she's a magician. My sister Hedy, she's going to be a treasure hunter, a Bess. And Max is . . . he's Max.'

'My mum says I'm a magnet for trouble,' said Max.

'Trouble like that?' Ines pointed at the gauntlet.

Max nodded.

'A man of quality.' She eyed Lark. 'And you, madame?'

Lark bowed her head sheepishly. 'I'm here by accident.'

With a swish of cool air, Simon let his form appear. He bowed and introduced himself in his native tongue. Ines bowed in return.

'Madame,' said Hedy, 'something is wrong with magic. The Spellbound Tree is weakening. We were told its heart of fire needs to be relit. Our grandfather was going to do it, but he and all the magicians have been trapped in one way or another. There's no one left to do it but us.'

At Ines's stricken look, Jelly added, 'Don't worry, we're not happy about it either. Unless you can . . . I mean, can *you* do whatever needs doing?'

Ines shook her head. 'I come back as guardian of the Ember Book. But I cannot journey to the Spellbound Tree.' She looked around them. 'The fire cannot be relit by anything other than a chalkydri.'

'Lucky for us,' said Spencer, 'we have one.'

Hedy reached into the middle of the pile of bear and fawn that hadn't stopped wrestling, and tugged Chalky out.

Ines slipped her hat off her ghostly head reverently. 'I never saw one in all my years.' She glanced at Fossile. 'With the Ember Book, the missing page and the chalkydri, we can open the gateway to the Spellbound Tree. This is something we shall remember, *ma chérie.*'

She reached out towards the book she had left behind, and ran a finger over the hairline gap between the book and the page. Fossile's curiosity finally overcame her fear and she gazed at the apparition of her partner with so much fascination and yearning that

Hedy had to swallow a lump in her throat.

Feeling intrusive, she dropped her eyes to the book. The gap between the torn edges glowed and then the fibres of paper began to knit together, repairing themselves, erasing the tear of the past. When it looked completely whole, Ines asked Fossile to close the book.

The embossed design on the cover was moving. The flame shapes in the heart of the tree began to dance, the lines of gold leaf flickering in the green leather.

Chalky yanked forwards in Hedy's hands with astounding force, chittering.

'Chalky!' she chided, willing him to settle so she could keep hold of him.

But something strange happened when she blinked. Just like the moment right before Lark had been freed, an image and a feeling flashed in her mind. The Ember Book filled her view. The flame shapes in its leather cover were silently pleading to be set free, and she knew the way to do it was to give it a hot spark to invite them out . . .

*I'm in Chalky's head again*, she thought, *I didn't imagine it!*

The little creature yipped at the book in Fossile's hands, letting out a lick of emerald-green flame. The

Ember Book caught immediately. But it didn't burn the colour of normal fire, or even green like Chalky's. The Ember Book's burgeoning fire was multi-hued – streaks of pink and blue, flecks of yellow and green, dashes of orange, silver, gold and mauve.

'Keep hold, my darling,' Ines said to the nervous Fossile. 'The chalkydri's green flame is the spark that had to ignite the Ember Book. Now look!'

Chalky strained towards the burning book and snapped at it.

'He's eating the flames!' Max said.

'He is the only creature that can,' said Ines.

With each bite and nip, hunks of the Ember Book's fire came away and he swallowed them with relish. All sorts of colours began to twine through his scales and fur.

'Listen carefully,' said Ines. 'He must take that many-coloured fire to the heart of the Spellbound Tree. But as a creature of fire, the chalkydri is a double-edged sword. He is necessary to save the tree, but he is also a danger to it. His own green flame is more powerful than ordinary fire. Uncontrolled, a chalkydri's fire can burn and destroy almost anything, including the Spellbound Tree.'

'Magicians aren't great at dummy-proof plans, are they?' sighed Jelly.

Ines frowned. 'Many things can be either a tool or weapon. The one who wields it must decide which it will be. So it is now. You must guard and guide the chalkydri and make sure he does not let his fire escape anywhere else.'

Chalky ate so fast that before any harm had come to Fossile, the Ember Book was gone. He let loose a little smoky burp.

A gust of wind blew through the reading room.

'The way to the Spellbound Tree is about to open,' whispered Ines.

The far side of the room began to transform. Its high arched panels, painted with trees and sky, deepened to look three-dimensional, an actual vista. The shelving below them was undergoing an even more extraordinary metamorphosis. It bulged and twisted, turned inside out and changed colour, became part of a forest that had grown from the painted scenes on the walls.

'This is like at the Dodo Manège!' Hedy murmured.

Ines nodded. 'Because it is the same family of magic.'

Real trees moved in the wind that was making Hedy's hair dance. The leaves and branches were not paint on plaster any more – they were *there*.

Wherever *there* was. The time was different in that place. It was morning here in Paris but some distance away, over the leafy canopy, rose one tremendous tree, silhouetted against a sunset.

'We've done it,' said Spencer. 'That's the Spellbound Tree, right?'

It was an arresting sight, that enormous tree swaying above the others. They were all so spellbound by the forest that had suddenly appeared that none of them knew what was happening until it was too late.

Lark grabbed Chalky and ran for the threshold between the library and the forest.

Bewildered, Hedy called out, 'Lark, what are you doing? Wait for us!'

But Lark ran a few more steps before she turned and held up her hand. In her fist was Grandpa John's snow globe. 'Stay back,' she cried out, 'or I smash this on the ground.'

They stared at her, dumbfounded. What on earth was happening?

Tempest was the first to recover. 'The rogue magician.' She growled and spread her wings to launch at the nurse.

Lark backed up further. 'Stay still, or when this hits the ground, John will be gone for ever.'

'No, don't!' Spencer cried.

Everyone stopped in their tracks. Max frantically whispered for someone to tell him what was going on, but nobody could put their fear into words.

'Why are you doing this?' Hedy pleaded.

Lark gave her a heartbroken look. 'Because magic is my calling. It's what I was born to do.' Her face turned defiant. 'But it turned on me, so I found a new purpose.'

'Killing magic?' Jelly was incredulous. 'Couldn't you volunteer for a charity or something like a normal person?'

Lark eyed her sharply. 'Shallow words. Exactly what I'd expect from a shallow girl.'

On their last adventure, Hedy had felt the terror of a rope bridge collapsing beneath her feet, with a deep chasm waiting to swallow her below. Realizing who Lark was felt like a slow-motion version of that moment. What Hedy had thought she knew was breaking apart, and the terrible truth was now engulfing her.

As Lark's feet shuffled from the library's wooden floor to the forest earth, the trees swayed, agitated. She edged into the forest further, hair swirling as the wind grew, blowing earth and leaves into the library.

'Chalky!' Doug yelled, dashing forwards, too fast for Hedy to catch.

Stan was right on his tail. 'We'll save you!'

In a whisper-roar of wind, the trunks and branches of the forest began to warp. They criss-crossed into a grid of wooden shelves, and leaves grew and reshaped, binding themselves as books again. It was all changing back.

Hedy unfroze, and hurtled towards the boundary. She dimly heard Spencer and Jelly running after her. Doug and Stan scurried over the threshold but the rest of them were all too late. The wind died and the smell of leaves and earth faded. With a smack, Hedy found herself colliding with book spines and wooden shelving.

As she blinked in pain, an image and a feeling flashed in her mind: she was a small creature surrounded by looming trees and strange sounds under a darkening sky. The only familiar face and voice left nearby was holding her, so she curled into their hands.

Hedy stumbled back, and Chalky's thought faded. He and Lark were gone. Stan and Doug too. And the gateway to the Spellbound Tree was lost.

## CHAPTER 20

### DOORS AND STEPS

Hedy pulled at books on the shelf in front of her, flinging them to the ground. Nothing extraordinary was behind them.

'Grandpa John!' she yelled.

It was irrational, she knew, because he hadn't been able to hear their voices when she held his snow globe in her hand, so there was no chance he'd hear while he was still trapped *and* in some other place. There was no sign of Doug or Stan. No hint of Chalky's thoughts. She pounded at the shelving, achieving nothing except two sore hands. It was Tempest who finally nudged her to give up.

'What just happened?' asked Spencer. He stared disbelievingly at where the forest had just been.

'Lark is the one trying to kill magic,' said Hedy heavily. 'She basically admitted it.'

'But . . .' Spencer squeezed his eyes shut, trying to make sense of everything. 'But she was *nice*. She was there to look after Grandpa John.'

'I bet she's not really a nurse or carer or whatever,' said Jelly. 'Remember, we couldn't find any sign of what hospital she was working for in her bag.'

*Dance*, Lark had told Hedy. *But I was injured. I'd dedicated so much of my life to it and then I couldn't do it any more.* She hadn't really been talking about dance, but about magic.

Hedy began running every moment with Lark through her head with a different lens, piecing together the subtle clues that should have put her on alert, if only she'd paid attention. How worried Lark had been about the time that morning – probably knowing the Morpheus Web was due to go off soon around the UK. Had Grandpa John caught Lark trying to steal his own Rosetta Jumbler in his study, and somehow turned the magic on her just when she was trapping him? Had she done something to Smithy, trapping him in the plate as he had freed her?

Even last night, she'd been eager to get her hands on the page in Mr Grutz's metal tube, keen to make Chalky come to her. When the water splash had woken Hedy and she'd found Lark with the tube in her hand . . . Hedy now had a feeling the Seine itself had been warning her about the page of the Ember Book being taken.

Lark must have had it planned for weeks, if not months. Somehow, she had learnt which magician was on a mission to heal the Spellbound Tree, and she'd preyed upon him. What would Lark do with Grandpa John? Toss his snow globe into the forest, never to be seen again? Hedy's mind began to tumble with such black thoughts that she wished she could turn her imagination off altogether.

'How do we follow her?' she asked Ines urgently.

The ghost frowned. 'I do not know. I did not make the gateway. The Ember Book was the task appointed to me. How the chalkydri opened the gateway may not even be something we can replicate.'

'But we need to open it again. She has my grand-father and our friends! Our entire family may be lost for ever if we don't stop her from hurting the Spell-bound Tree.'

Ines's form was more transparent and her voice sounded fainter than before. 'The gateway is closed because the chalkydri has passed through. It cannot be opened now.'

'How can we open another one?'

'Our only hope is to ask the Conjuror. He was the one who made *this* gateway and the Ember Book.'

'But he'd have to be dead by now,' said Jelly, before remembering their present company. 'Er, not that we don't like dead people, madame.'

Ines seemed to be disappearing by degrees. Her ghostly form appeared and disappeared with the rhythm of a slowing heartbeat. Sounding more distant than ever, she said, 'You must seek out the Conjurer in the catacombs below the second arrondissement.'

'But the catacombs are only open in the fourteenth,' warned Fossile.

'That is for tourists,' said Ines. 'There are more tunnels open than that. I do not have long left here. Listen carefully, *ma chérie*. And you, Monsieur de Polignac.' She signalled for Simon to join them and spoke quickly to them both in French.

'She described the way to the Conjuror,' Simon explained when Ines had finished. 'Fossile will show us the nearest entrance.'

'To where?' Spencer asked.

'To the empire of the dead.'

'Well *that* sounds inviting,' Jelly muttered.

'Go now,' Ines told them. Then she turned to Fossile and took a long look, as though it would have to last her for the rest of time.

Fossile's face crumpled. She reached out a hand but Ines twitched away, saying, 'No, you must not touch me.'

Hedy knew what worried her: the cold touch of the dead that could eventually take life if left unchecked. She glanced out of the large windows. 'Sunlight will cure the chill,' she said. When Ines didn't look convinced, she added, 'It's happened to me.'

'Me too,' said Spencer. 'We poked Simon once.'

Fossile nodded in thanks. 'You see?' she said to Ines, lifting her face with a stubborn expression. They kissed and held each other's gaze as Ines Impossible dwindled and faded away. Another minute passed, but this time she did not come back.

*

They followed Fossile through the back corridors of the library, past offices and a staff kitchen (where Spencer and Max filched some small packets of biscuits) to an old fire exit door. She checked to make sure no one else was about, pushed the door open, and then closed it. She opened and closed it a second time, and then a third. On the fourth time, she held the door open and beckoned them through to a dimly lit, dusty staircase.

'Ines said that at the bottom of these stairs is a way to the catacombs,' said Fossile. 'It is only revealed by opening the door the way I did just then and jumping over the last two steps at the bottom. Come.'

With Fossile leading them, they descended six flights of steps until another door appeared at the bottom. It had the usual fire exit sign like the door they'd hurried through – a white stick figure on a green background, running in the direction of an arrow that pointed to the right.

Hedy looked around at the others, and then lightly jumped from the third-last step to the ground. She half expected a transformation of the stairwell just as in the grand reading room, but it seemed to look the same. She wondered if Ines had gotten things wrong.

Then her eyes swept over the exit sign again. Instead of pointing right, the arrow now angled left and downwards. She shoved the door open. A gloomy tunnel stretched away from the light of the stairwell.

'*Oui*, that is it,' said Simon. 'I can feel them.'

One by one, the others sprang down to join Hedy at the tunnel entrance until Fossile was the only one left on the stairs.

'Should I join you?' she asked, gripping the banister as though readying herself for the jump.

Hedy shook her head. 'You should find some sunshine before the chill takes you.' She suddenly worried for Fossile, as though they'd known her for much longer than this dreadful short morning. 'And tomorrow too. If you wake with a chill tomorrow, you'll do the same, won't you?'

Fossile nodded. 'I will ask my children to dine with me tonight, *and* check on me tomorrow.'

Hedy felt better at that. 'We're sorry.'

'Why are you sorry?'

'We sort of turned up and made a huge mess and your book got burnt.'

Behind her daisy-frame glasses, Fossile's eyes were red but not sad. 'You also let me see Ines one last time.'

'Do you think it was the last time?' asked Spencer.

'It may be,' said Fossile. 'Although I like to imagine it is not. Imagination is a powerful thing, is it not?' She smiled at them. 'I imagine you will get to the tree. I want you to promise to tell me all about it, when we next meet. Agreed?'

Max answered for them all. 'Deal!'

With a final wave at Fossile, they made their way through the door to the Paris catacombs.

## CHAPTER 21

## THE EMPIRE OF THE DEAD

Hedy led the way, torch in hand. The tunnel quickly narrowed and after they had walked for some time, they came across a shaft in the floor.

'Down this way,' said Simon. 'We make our way to the Crossroads of the Dead.'

Jelly shivered. 'Are you sure? How do you know where to go?'

'The dead can feel where the dead are.'

'Is that a good thing or a bad thing in a zombie apocalypse?'

Hedy had to tie Simon's piano stool to her by the

troll's whisker and let it dangle underneath her as she descended the rungs punched into the side of the shaft. By the light of the torch, she saw pencil markings on the walls, people's names, dates a hundred years old or more. They climbed down around twenty metres before reaching yet another tunnel.

'Now you may walk the rest of the way,' Simon said. 'Or crawl if it becomes a snug fit.'

The further they went, the more uneasy Hedy became. The tunnel wasn't like the slipways from Hoarder Hill and Edinburgh that she had travelled – slipways she'd always unthinkingly assumed were stable thanks to magical buttressing. This tunnel was cramped and there were frequent puddles of dirty water. Rumbles overhead – which Simon said were trains – made the tunnel shake.

At school camp last year, a boy in her class had discovered he had a fear of heights only after he was trapped up high in a climbing activity, sliding his feet over the slacklines strung between the treetops, many metres off the ground. He'd frozen, unable to move forward or back until one of the camp staff had come to guide him down. At the time, Hedy had remembered her own daring run across disappearing rope bridges in Puzzlewood and grumbled at the hold-up. Now, however, she chided herself. She wasn't any more fearless than the next kid.

'I hope there aren't tunnel collapses down here,' she said, fishing for an encouraging word from Simon who floated in front.

'They do happen, I believe,' the ghost admitted.

'For crying out loud, Simon!' Jelly exclaimed. 'Hedy's about to have a freak-out. Can't you be more positive?'

'Do not bellow so loudly down here, Jelly, unless you want to *cause* a collapse,' said Simon. He turned around to look at Hedy, continuing to float backwards. 'Are you claustrophobic or fearful of the dead?'

'A little bit of the first one,' said Hedy. 'I keep imagining it crumbling down on us.'

'If that is your worry,' said Simon comfortingly, 'rest easy. Since you are not afraid of the dead, you'll have six million or so for company down here.'

It was a dark joke, but it made Hedy laugh anyway. She started to feel the black fingers of fear release their hold just a little, just enough.

'Six *million*?' Jelly visibly shuddered. 'That really is an empire of the dead.'

'I reckon everything just sounds creepier when you add "of the dead" at the end,' Spencer piped up. Hedy was surprised at how easily her younger brother was handling the dank tunnel.

'Not everything,' said Max. 'Some things sound funnier.'

'Such as?'

Max thought a moment. 'Shin pads of the dead.'

They all exploded in giggles.

'Burrito of the dead,' tried Spencer.

'Drainpipe of the dead?' offered Tempest.

That did it; all of them tried to outdo each other with absurd turns of phrase. *Lipstick of the dead. Porridge of the dead. Lawnmower of the dead. Deodorant of the dead.* When they got to *toilet paper of the dead,* they had covered enough ground that Simon clapped his hands and told them they had reached their destination.

'Where?' said Hedy. The tunnel seemed to have reached a dead end.

Simon pointed to a square hole cut in the tunnel wall. 'This is the way through. Catacomb explorers use these. You must crawl through it. My piano stool will not fit through, but you may leave it here. The dead are just on the other side.'

Heart jumping like a frog in her ribs, Hedy crawled through the square gap.

Catacombs were underground passages for burying dead bodies, so she'd imagined a stack of sarcophagi or decaying wooden coffins, maybe skeletons with the remains of their clothes, lying in neat recesses. Perhaps a part of her had been imagining a chamber full of ghosts, wafty and see-through like Simon and Ines, lined up and looking at them with judgement in their eyes for daring to come in here.

She hadn't been expecting branching tunnels, filled with untidy piles of long leg bones and broken skulls. They weren't white bones either. They were a grimy brown colour, like rotted teeth.

Jelly covered her mouth with her hands. 'This is the most revolting place I've ever been. And I've been under Max's bed.'

Spencer sniffed experimentally. 'At least it doesn't smell.'

'All the flesh must have decomposed before they tossed the bones in here,' said Jelly. 'Meat falling off like lamb shanks in a slow cooker.'

'Jelly, do you have to?' hissed Hedy.

'Sorry. It's that babbling worried, nervous thing I do when I'm stuck underground with millions of human skeletons.'

Hedy was glad they hadn't had a big breakfast that morning. 'Simon, what do we do now? How do we talk to the Conjuror?'

Simon peered down one branching tunnel and then another and another. 'We must call for his aid.'

He began to speak rapidly in French, facing down each of the diverging passageways in turn. His entreaty echoed eerily off the walls. After a few minutes of this, an indistinct rattle could be heard down one of the tunnels. It grew louder and louder. Something was moving down there. Hedy didn't mind at all when Spencer gripped her hand. Femurs and chipped craniums in the tunnel surged up and down, clattering in a macabre wave. Something surfed towards them on the top of that swell of bones – round, lopsided, brownish. It stopped at their feet, a skull with its lower jaw missing.

Hedy held her breath as the skull twisted in place, its black eye sockets sweeping over each of them. *It's just a head bone, not a monster*, she told herself, but her mouth went desert-dry with fear.

'You dare to unsettle the empire of the dead?' said the skull. Despite its missing lower jaw, it spoke with a deep, silken voice, quiet with anger. It turned to Simon. 'And you, you are dead. You should know better.'

'P-pardon, monsieur,' Hedy stammered. 'Are you the Conjuror?'

The skull said nothing, so Hedy plunged on. 'Ines Impossible sent us to find you. She said the Conjuror may be able to help us reach the Spellbound Tree. It's in danger.'

'I already created a gateway,' said the Conjuror.

'We know. We just came from the Richelieu Library,' said Hedy. 'The gateway's closed. But someone who means to destroy the tree went through it with a chalkydri. We need to stop her.'

The skull muttered harshly to itself in French and then snapped, 'How could such a thing be allowed to happen? Do modern magicians have feet for brains? Are they so stupid and weak they allow useless children to be the protectors of magic?'

Hedy squirmed, sharing a humiliated look with the others.

'Magicians may have feet for brains,' grated

Tempest. 'But these children are far from useless. This commission fell to them by bad fortune and yet they have never shied from it. They may be young for champions, but champions they are.'

The Conjuror sniffed, then said, 'Let me see if you speak the truth. You, girl, come closer.'

A shiver went through Hedy. She squeezed Spencer's hand before letting go and edging closer to the skull. 'Here?'

'Closer, young champion.' Hedy sensed the Conjuror's sarcasm. 'I cannot see unless you put your fingers where my eyes would be.'

'Into your *eye* sockets?'

'Unless you think my eyes would be in my nose holes,' he mocked.

Swallowing the urge to retch, Hedy crouched by the skull and did as he had asked, holding a trembling finger in each of the skull's vacant eye sockets.

The Conjuror let out a satisfied sigh. Gradually, Hedy's mind began to whirl, memories and sensations playing like a jumbled movie in her head. She ricocheted from the heat of the Ember Book in the library to the Morpheus Web explosion at Hoarder Hill. From laughter at Chalky stuck under Violette's couch to Tempest flying over the Seine. The feel of the sivatherium's fur. The glint of the sword in Max's hand. Damp mist as Spencer's cloud animal burst in the garage.

And then the Conjuror reached even further into her past, scanning their past adventures as though riffling through a catalogue. Air rushing in her ears as she flew with Grandpa John inside a dark painted world. The salty smell of the sea as they raced a giant at the Giant's Causeway. Vertigo as the whirlpool sucked their canoe down in the cave of the Kelpie King. Terror as they ran over disintegrating bridges in Puzzlewood. Dread and pride when the magician's map flowed into her skin.

Hedy wanted to wrest back control, but he continued to rummage in her mind, unearthing fragments she'd tried to bury. Envy when Jelly was recognized as a *magicienne* by the Whisper. The hurt of Lark's betrayal. Icy fear upon realizing their parents had disappeared. The smell of the trees when Grandpa John crumpled to the ground in Foxwood.

'Enough,' said the Conjuror finally.

Hedy yanked her fingers from the skull, feeling ragged.

With a new note of respect, he said, 'The gargoyle did not lie. You are not as ordinary as you all appear. And I perceive *you* are the bearer of a living map.'

Hedy unconsciously touched the small black mark behind her ear, a little part of the magician's map that had stuck with her. 'Yes, sir.'

'That is an immense privilege.'

*I know I should* feel *that it is*, she thought.

'Will it help us get to the Spellbound Tree, sir?' Spencer asked.

The skull rolled around, not saying a word.

'What's he doing?' Max whispered.

'Pacing?' Spencer whispered back. 'Since he's, you know, missing his legs and everything.'

At last, the Conjuror halted his spinning about. 'There is a slim hope. You have a living map. You have the sword. And you have a *magicienne*. If I channel the young *magicienne*'s magic, perhaps you can reach the place where the nearest threshold appears, where the map and sword can take you through.'

'Where is that?' asked Hedy.

'The border between countries, at the border between time.' As they stared uncomprehending at him, the skull explained, 'France's border with

England. At midnight, the time we cross from one day to the next.'

'In the middle of the Channel?' Hedy began to feel a flutter of panic. 'How do we get out there? Swim?'

The Conjuror snorted. 'Do you expect the threshold to the Spellbound Tree to be so attainable that any ordinary simpleton could pass through it? That is why I created the library gateway in the first place, because the threshold in the Channel is so much more difficult.' The black eye sockets fixed on Spencer. 'The fates gifted you a skyskepnur, and now I think you know the reason why. You will need magic of course.' He sighed doubtfully. 'I fear her magic is not strong enough.'

'Well, hang on,' spluttered Jelly. 'I graduated from moving acne to moving extinct animals pretty fast.'

'Can you come with us, sir?' Hedy asked. 'You said you could channel Jelly's magic.'

But the skull shook from side to side. 'No, I cannot journey to the Spellbound Tree. The best I can do is amplify the *magicienne*'s ability to get you as close to the threshold as possible.' He twisted to face Simon. 'I will need Monsieur de Polignac's help.'

## CHAPTER 22

## A PIANO OF BONES

Once the Conjuror had explained what he needed to do, all of them looked glumly at Simon. None of them quite knew what to say except for Max.

'I don't want Simon to stay behind!' he said heatedly. 'He's one of us. Isn't there another way?'

'I need music to augment your sister's power,' said the Conjuror firmly. 'Not only to moor the living map, not only to open the slipway, but it is also necessary to keep the slipway open so that the earth does not swallow you. There is no other way in the time we have.

Not if you are to stop this Lark woman. She had to cover some distance to get to the Spellbound Tree, from the library gateway, but who knows how far she has travelled by now?'

'Why music?' said Max stubbornly.

'Music and magic are related. Everyone knows that.'

'It is necessary, young Max,' said Simon gently. 'It is one way I can truly help.'

But Max was on the verge of tears. 'We keep losing everyone. All our parents and grandparents. Bess and Violette. Lark was a stinking, tricky traitor. Doug and Stan are gone.' He dashed a fist across his eyes. 'What if we all end up separated?'

'You're not getting rid of me that easily, silly,' said Jelly with a rough hug.

Hedy edged as close to Simon's cool form as she dared. 'Simon, are you OK staying here?'

'I dislike being parted from you, my dear friends,' said Simon, 'but I do not fear it. I cannot turn my back on this role if I am the only one to fill it.'

The Conjuror clattered on the ground for their attention. 'The hands of the clock do not lie still. It nears midday. We must begin, lest you miss the threshold at midnight. Jelly?'

Jelly let go of Max, crossed over to the brown skull and lifted it to her forehead. 'For the record, mind-melding with a grubby old skull is not my idea of a good time.'

'Be quiet and focus,' the Conjuror admonished her. 'Focus on where you can feel magic.'

'Right. Heartburn.'

A hush fell over the chamber. Faintly, down the branching tunnels, Hedy heard a rustle, a click of bones, a squeak. She hoped it wasn't rats.

And then into the quiet, Jelly began to speak. She was giving voice to fluent, rapid French, which they all knew she was not capable of. The Conjuror was talking through her.

Even as the words poured out of Jelly's mouth, her eyes darted about wild and frightened. Yet she resolutely kept her forehead pressed to that of the skull. The bones of the catacombs began to jitter and clatter, like a thousand castanets being shaken at once. A wave of them rose up and amassed, as though an unseen spirit was creating something with gruesome building blocks. Leg bones, arm bones, slender finger bones stacked together until they formed a familiar shape. It was a piano.

Jelly and the Conjuror's words lowered to a barely discernible whisper. Simon floated to a pile of bones fashioned into a piano stool in front of the skeleton piano. He gracefully arched his wrists, and then pressed the finger bones that served as the keys of his eerie instrument.

There were no wires in this piano to make sound, but every finger bone key played a ghostly voice of a different pitch. By playing the piano, Simon was commanding a chorus of the singing dead. Hedy recognized the piece. It was his concerto.

A smile spread across Simon's face as he played on, the catacombs resounding with the melody of his pride and joy. The longer he played, the more voices hung in the air, filling the passageways and tunnels. Hedy began to feel a rise in pressure around them at the suspended notes.

Dust fell as the tunnels themselves quaked. Hedy put her arms around Spencer and Max, and she felt Tempest spread her wings protectively at her back. They prepared to brace against falling rock, perhaps the collapse of the whole chamber, perhaps the failure of everything.

The bronze nail on Jelly's finger began to radiate

light. A hair-thin beam grew from it, like a glowing spider's thread wafting in the wind.

'Hedy, hold still,' Jelly called out.

Hedy forced herself to stay in place as the beam coiled through the air towards her. She felt a tugging behind her ear where the wisp of the magician's map remained, calling the thread of light. *I cannot turn my back on this role if I am the only one to fill it*, Simon had said. Then neither could Hedy. She forced herself to remain steady. When the thread of light fused with the magician's map, she felt it snake its way into her skin, wriggling from her neck down through her body and arms.

Simon's concerto continued to build, and Jelly's nail began to pulse with near-blinding rays. Then with a thunderous tremor, one passageway of bones streamed away, clearing a new path from the crossroads of the dead. Hedy sensed the pull of the magician's map in her skin immediately, begging her to travel along the new slipway that the Conjuror and Jelly had created.

Slowly, the quaking of the catacombs eased. Jelly reeled and the skull dropped from her hand.

'We have done it,' said the Conjuror. 'Go forth now. You must travel this slipway quickly, for it is hasty work and does not shorten distances as much as others do. Monsieur de Polignac, you must continue playing for as long as you can to keep the slipway open. Do not fail your young friends.'

Hedy helped Jelly to her feet and then with Spencer and Max they clustered by Simon, who played unceasingly on the piano of bones.

'I shall not fail you, my friends,' he said. 'And I feel we shall meet again.'

'Do you mean at Hoarder Hill,' asked Spencer, 'or are you making an afterlife joke?'

Simon smiled. 'Hurry along. Bring the Master back safely.'

Clinging to Simon's promise they would see him again, Hedy led them towards the slipway. 'Monsieur,' she said, pausing in front of the Conjuror's skull, 'thank you.'

The Conjuror nodded. 'For the sake of my past life, I wish you success. Follow the map. It should bring you to the coast, where La Seine meets the sea. But take care, for magic close to the Spellbound Tree is stronger, wilder. It may change you.'

'This guy needs to work on his goodbyes,' Jelly said under her breath.

They waved at Simon until they rounded the bend of the slipway. Hedy had a lump in her throat when they lost sight of him. Even with Tempest bringing up the rear, their group felt too small. The only comfort was the sound of his concerto following them well after they left the crossroads.

Being so new and (from what the Conjuror had said) so fragile, the slipway was uneven along the ground and walls. Dirt and rock dust was easily dislodged by their passing. Worms could be seen wriggling in surprise at the gaping tunnel that hadn't been there a short time ago. Every now and then, the slipway crossed another cluster of catacombs, but none of the human remains in them moved.

'Hey, I've got a joke,' said Jelly. 'How does the Conjuror open the door to the catacombs?'

'How?' asked Spencer.

'With a skeleton key.'

They all groaned, but a minute later, Spencer said, 'OK, I've got one. How does the Conjuror know something bad is about to happen?'

'How?' Hedy asked.

'Cos he feels it in his bones.'

'Welcome to the Dad Joke Olympics!' Jelly declared.

Hedy shook her head and set her watch alarm for midnight. 'This is going to be a long walk.'

It turned out to be an even longer walk than Hedy thought. The rumbling of the Paris metro system became a distant memory and the echoes of the chorus of dead voices trailed off. For hours, they trudged along, putting their trust in the map in Hedy's skin. They drank sparingly from their water bottles and rationed the biscuits that Spencer and Max had taken from the Richelieu Library staff kitchen.

Sometimes Max called out for a break, and they'd stop to sit against the slipway walls, overworked feet tingling. Jelly took the Conjuror's words to heart, and whenever they sat to rest, she hummed snippets of Simon's concerto, hoping to keep the slipway open and stable.

The changes in the rock and earth told them they were shifting landscape, but they resorted to plodding in exhausted silence, wondering when on earth they would reach the end.

At long last, Hedy felt the pull of the map change and twist. 'I think we're getting close,' she told the others.

The slipway ended by spilling them into a brick-work tunnel. From the tunnel there was a shaft that led upwards to a manhole cover. A car passed overhead. When there was no sound of another vehicle approaching, Hedy and Jelly pushed at the heavy manhole cover and flipped it open. They crawled out as quickly as they could, dragged the boys up and then let Tempest flap her way to the surface as well. Grunting and straining, they awkwardly got the manhole cover back in place.

They had emerged in the middle of a road that travelled alongside the sea. The air was humid and they seemed to be close to a town.

The map was rippling in Hedy's skin, but its eagerness had an expectant *nearly there* quality, rather than *here we are*.

Given the hour, there weren't a lot of cars, but they scurried off the road before another one chanced upon them, and through a skate park. Beyond it lay the beach, austere in the bright light of the moon.

The urge of the map intensified so suddenly that Hedy stumbled. It wanted to rush beyond the sand to the water's edge, into the Channel itself. It craved the silver pathway of moonlight on the water. That's where it belonged.

A wrench of her arm pulled Hedy up short. It was Jelly. Hedy hadn't realized she'd been running and had been about to launch herself into the Channel.

Jelly scanned the sea. 'Is that where we have to go?'

'Yeah.' Hedy breathed deeply to bring herself under control.

'I guess we've walked across ocean waters before,' said Jelly.

'But there's no slipway bridge over the water here. And I don't think we can swim to the threshold,' said Hedy. She checked her watch. 'We've only got fifteen minutes until midnight.'

Spencer slung his backpack to the sand and unstrapped his skyskepnur. 'Time to try this out again.'

## CHAPTER 23

## PATH OF THE MOON

Dancing to keep his trainers dry at the water line, Spencer filled the leather bulb of the skyskepnur device, then reattached it.

'I think the glue worked,' he said with a hopeful half-smile.

He stood and waved it through the air, turning its fishing-rod-like handle and watching the mist in the net closely. When he judged it formed enough, he swung downwards to let the cloud animal detach.

It was a small dragon with a long, arched neck and two unfurled wings that were, unfortunately, different sizes. They waited and waited but the cloud dragon failed to grow bigger. It only drifted along the beach and eventually deteriorated.

Spencer looked at Hedy forlornly. 'It's not good enough.'

'Jelly, can you help?' Hedy asked her cousin.

Spencer moved to hand the rod to her, but Jelly held up both hands. 'Not taking over this time. Helping you. Try it again, but bigger.'

Spencer swept the net from side to side, and then began tracing a larger pattern through the air as though he were in some sort of flag-waving competition. Watching intently, Jelly waited until the mist in the net was dense and thick and then she said, 'Now.'

With a jerk of the net, Spencer released the cloud – another dragon. Jelly bounced forwards and began pulling at its edges, her bronze fingernail radiating. The cloud dragon began to balloon to the size of a pig, then a horse, but the more Jelly increased the size, the more shapeless it became. Soon it was the size of an elephant, but the form of the dragon was lost. The light from Jelly's fingernail began to ebb, like a torch stuttering. And then a gust of wind blew off the water, breaking the cloud apart entirely. Hedy choked back a cry as wisps of mist puffed past her, refusing to be held by her clutching fingers. *We're not going to make this work in time*, she thought, glancing at her watch.

'What the heck is that?' Max asked. His unease had prompted the sword to shoot out from his gauntlet, and he pointed it out at the water.

Moonlight glimmered off a head and shoulders rising from the water of the Channel. Was it some late-night swimmer? The four of them huddled together closely. Uncharacteristically, Tempest also gathered by them, hiding timidly behind their legs.

Long hair, limbs and skin of water, black as the night sky above them, reflecting moon and stars. They knew this figure. They had seen her whilst riding the lost creatures of the carousel. It was the naiad who had created the wave at the Pont Neuf.

'What's she doing here? Stalking us?' Spencer asked in a strangled tone.

'The Conjuror said he'd get us to where La Seine meets the sea,' Hedy whispered. 'And I'm sure she's the spirit of the River Seine.'

The naiad rose until all but her feet were above the water and began to walk towards them. She stopped where the tide washed upon the sand and beckoned them closer.

'Can we trust her?' said Spencer.

'She saved us once,' said Hedy. 'Maybe she's going to help us again. Come on.'

Moving like a ten-legged animal, they scuttled down to the water's edge and waved to the naiad hesitantly.

Just as she had near the bridge, the naiad gathered water in her hands to shape it into the image of the immense tree with three broad roots and fire inside its trunk. She swept her hand out from the shore towards England and the tree shot away from her, along the path of reflected moonlight, and disappeared in the black.

'Yes, we know,' called Hedy. 'We need to travel to the threshold.'

The naiad pointed to the skyskepnur in Spencer's hand. He bit his lip. 'You want this? But it's how we'll cross the water.'

The naiad made a vexed sound, as though he hadn't understood her. With a tilt of the head, she sent a stream of water from her finger to the bulb of the skyskepnur.

'Oh!' Spencer exclaimed. He scrambled with the cap of the bulb and held it open so that the water flowing from the naiad's finger was caught inside it. On and on it streamed, much more than the bulb should have been able to hold. Finally, the bulb started to overflow and she stopped the flow of water. When Spencer had tightened the cap again, she gestured at the device and the space around them.

'We're to try again,' Spencer said.

They backed away from the water's edge and, watched by the naiad, made their third attempt at creating a cloud animal. Spencer waved the net in wide arcs to and fro, muttering to himself. He jerked the net down, and released a white cloud dragon, the mist dense and sharply defined this time. Jelly skipped in, bronze nail shining again, and began coaxing the cloud dragon outwards and upwards with her hands.

It grew steadily, bigger than an ox, then an elephant, then a small house. The shape held steady, even when another strong gust of wind blew sand against their legs. A tail snaked between them, and great wings stretched into the night above the beach.

The cloud dragon swung its head towards Spencer. It blinked, and seemed to be waiting for orders.

'M-mighty dragon . . . will you fly us to the Spell-bound Tree, please?' stammered Spencer.

The dragon snorted deferentially, sending a wisp of cloud into their faces, cool and dewy. Then it reared its head and plucked them one by one with its teeth by the scruff of their sweaters. Hedy held in her squeak of fright. She should have passed through vapour and landed on the sand but instead, she sat a few metres off the ground, between the wings of a cloud dragon. In front of her were Max and Spencer, and Jelly was behind.

Tempest flapped up to join them. 'I have never relied on the strength of wings other than my own,' she said. 'I confess that I am wary.'

'This is a first for all of us,' said Hedy, giving the gargoyle a pat on the head.

Spencer bowed to the naiad as best he could whilst sitting on a dragon. 'Thank you.'

She curtsied in return, and then gestured out towards the Channel, her meaning clear this time: *Go*.

As Spencer murmured to the dragon, Hedy placed her hands on the creature's back. It was damp, and a bit squishy, like cotton wool. To her shock, a writhing line of the map squirmed from her skin into the dragon's back, and burrowed inwards. The dragon shivered, and reared up on its legs, beat its mighty cloud wings and soared into the sky.

Glancing over her shoulder, Hedy saw the naiad ebbing away with each wave that washed in and out of the beach. She waved, hoping the spirit could see her.

'Should we have invited her to come with us?' asked Spencer. 'I feel bad we left her there on the beach.'

'In one sense she's with us,' said Hedy. 'I mean, it took her water to make this guy.'

Spencer looked happier at that.

'My underpants are wet,' said Max.

'Max, you should have told us before if you needed to go,' said Jelly.

'Not *that*, Jelly. They're wet because of the cloud.'

Hedy checked her watch. 'Two minutes to midnight.'

The dragon flew purposefully along the path of moonlight reflected in the dark water. Hunkering down to ward off the chill wind, Hedy hoped it knew where to go. It had been sunset when Lark had taken Grandpa John and Chalky to the land of the Spellbound Tree. She wondered if it was daytime there now, or if they'd be crossing into pitch-black night there too.

When her watch alarm trilled, the silver-white band of moonlight on the water disappeared. The moon itself hung in the sky, but it was as though a great magician had stolen its reflection, hidden it under a silken black cloth.

'That must be it,' said Hedy. 'The threshold.'

'But I can't see anything except dark,' said Jelly. 'Can you?'

The dragon jutted its head forwards, putting on a surge of speed that made all of them teeter dangerously. Jelly shrieked and grabbed Tempest's horns to stop from tumbling off over the dragon's tail.

After a few hundred metres, Spencer cried out, 'I can see something!'

Hedy raked her eyes over the Channel. Some distance away, a wall of water sprawled north and south. It was inky-black, tipped with churning water at the top. The ribbon of the moon's reflection that had disappeared was behind that wall of water. It made the map in her skin thrum.

'How do we get through that?' Max asked.

'Maybe it'll fall down when we get close,' Jelly hoped.

They streamed towards the wall of water, although

in its vast presence, even their cloud dragon seemed utterly insignificant. Its frothing top was as tall as a skyscraper, and it was clearly too long to fly around. Besides, Hedy knew that going around a threshold was not the same as crossing it.

The dragon brought them in close to the threshold but came to a stop just before it. Fine mist fell on them from on high as their cloud hung silently in front of the towering wall of water. The map in Hedy's skin was pulling so powerfully for the path beyond the wall that she could barely think. She had to get through. Suddenly, she dived from the dragon's back towards the wall of water, in thrall to the map, heedless of the others screaming at her to stop. The only thing that mattered was to pierce the threshold and reach the moonlight on the other side.

*Wham!* She bounced off the wall of water, nothing more than an insect bashing against glass. And then gravity took over. Screaming, Hedy fell down, fear puncturing the mesmerizing, dangerous pull of the map that had failed to take her over the threshold. How bad would the pain be when she hit the surface of the Channel? Would the impact kill her?

And then she jolted to a stop. She was dangling

upside down, blood rushing to her head, but not plunging to her death. Her scream trailing off to a whimper, Hedy looked up past her ankle. The cloud dragon had her right leg in its teeth. It had caught her.

Drawing its neck in, the cloud dragon reeled Hedy up to the safety of its back.

'Oh em fishing gee, Hedy,' said Jelly, flinging her arms around her. 'Are you OK?'

'I think I left all my insides somewhere else,' said Hedy faintly.

'What were you thinking?' Spencer demanded.

Hedy knew from the furrow between his brows how frightened he'd been. 'I wasn't. The map took over.'

'Uh-oh,' said Max, pointing at the wall of water. 'We might be too late.'

Patches of the immense threshold were disappearing. It was as though a tap had been turned off and the wall was fading. The ordinary Channel was becoming visible through the gaps.

'Map and sword,' rasped Tempest. 'The Conjuror said the map and sword could take us through.'

Hedy grasped the gauntlet on Max's hand and felt another line of the map roll in her skin and wriggle into the metal glove. Out shot the sword. They yelled at the dragon to fly towards one of the last remaining stretches of the threshold and together Hedy and Max plunged the tip of the blade into the wall of water.

The moon's reflection instantly intensified, illuminating them and carving a passage through the threshold. At Spencer's command, the cloud dragon swooped through.

## CHAPTER 24

## THE SPELLBOUND ISLE

They emerged into daylight, flying over a cold-looking bright sea. Blinking against the sudden appearance of the sun, Hedy turned to see the wall of water receding, lowering itself into dark, choppy waves. Beyond it, there was no sign of the French coast. Nothing but horizon.

Ahead, however, was an island with one colossal tree at its centre, taller than the forest surrounding it. The same forest they had seen from the library.

'There it is,' Hedy breathed. 'The Spellbound Tree.'

Max waved the sword over his head triumphantly.

'We did it!'

'Sit down, numbskull,' said Jelly. 'Now we have to find Uncle John and Chalky and Doug and Stan.'

'We head for the Spellbound Tree,' said Hedy. 'If Lark's not already there, that's where she'll be going.'

They huddled together as their cloud dragon soared above the island's steep, rocky slopes, and then over the forest canopy.

'Maybe it was a blessing in disguise we got here this way,' murmured Spencer. 'Imagine having to thrash your way through all of those trees! If we're lucky, we might beat Lark there.'

*But then what?* Hedy thought. She rubbed at the map beating insistently in her skin.

When they were within fifty metres of the Spell-bound Tree, Spencer murmured to the dragon and it slowed to a more cloud-like drift. At this distance, Hedy could see that big patches of the Spellbound Tree's leafy crown were yellowing or brown.

They descended through the forest. The dragon was unbothered by the boughs and foliage for it could simply break around them and re-form, but the rest of them were slapped and scraped as they went down. When the dragon floated to a stop, Hedy had to shake leaves out of her hair.

'Can you smell smoke?' Max asked.

Hedy clamped a hand over his lips and put a finger to her own. *Quiet.* But she nodded.

Jelly tapped her chest. 'I can feel the magic here, big time.'

'It's stronger here,' Tempest agreed. 'Stronger and wilder.'

They tiptoed towards the tree with the dragon stealing alongside them silently. It wafted around the tree trunks, tail undulating, like a pet fog.

Despite the unrelenting pull of the map, Hedy held up a hand to halt when the Spellbound Tree came into view. It was enormous. The trunk was ten metres or more in diameter. It rose at least fifty metres into the sky and part way up the trunk was a large hollow. Three massive roots anchored the tree to either side of a deep gorge. But unlike the naiad's water sculpture, and unlike the cover of Fossile's book, one of the roots was on fire.

'I can't see Lark,' whispered Spencer. 'Is that fire good? Is the tree re-ignited?'

Hedy shook her head. 'It's green, the dangerous kind. The many-coloured fire from the Ember Book should be set in that hollow. The tree's heart.'

Something small scampered out of the tree root that was on fire. It was Chalky. He seemed perfectly at ease and scurried to the next gnarled tree root, sniffing happily. It was hard to believe that a creature as endearing and cheery as him could be so dangerous.

Something else moved from behind the tree.

Tempest craned her head to see. 'Is that Doug? Or Stanley?'

It was Lark. She looked exactly like she had spent a day and night fighting her way through heavy-going forest. There was a smudge of dried mud on her cheek, a tear in the knee of her trousers and her grey cardigan was filthy. She crouched down to watch the burning tree root, her expression relieved, almost blissful.

Lark pulled something from her pocket, tore a little bit off and held it out to Chalky. He ate it from her fingers happily.

'I bet that's croissant,' Spencer scowled.

Lark reached out to scratch Chalky on the head and crooned softly, encouraging him. With a puppy-like wiggle, Chalky opened his jaws and shot a lick of flame at a second tree root. The fire took hold immediately.

'Why's Chalky doing that?' Max exclaimed.

'He's so little he doesn't know he's doing the wrong thing,' said Hedy. 'Especially when she's rewarding him with food.'

Exhilarated, Chalky turned his head and barked another thin jet of flame at the tree trunk itself.

'What do we do?' Spencer asked.

'Put out the green fire,' said Hedy bleakly. 'Stop Lark. Get Chalky. Light the heart of the tree.' It was a string of deceptively simple words. *What to do* was simple. She had no idea about the *how*.

A titanic groan swept through the forest. It was the Spellbound Tree. The map in Hedy's skin thrashed in a way it never had before, sensing the devastation Lark had set in train. The tree and perhaps their whole family was about to go up in flames. She had to stop it now.

Painfully aware that she had no real plan, Hedy strode forward anyway. With the Spellbound Tree's groan, Chalky had leapt into Lark's hands but, seeing Hedy, he chirruped and squirmed with excitement.

Lark's eyes went wide. For a moment she almost looked glad to see Hedy, as though she was in need of a friend. 'Hedy.' She paused and smiled. 'You're too late.'

'Lark, you have to stop it,' Hedy called out. Her

voice was shaky with dread. Were they too late? 'You said yourself that magic is your calling. You don't actually want to do this.'

'Once upon a time, it made me feel worthwhile and whole and alive,' said Lark. 'But I can't do it any more. I gave magic all I had, and I was rewarded by every tendril of magic being burnt out of me.' Her eyes glistened. 'I can't stand not being able to do it any more. Maybe if it doesn't exist, I'll stop feeling like I've lost it.'

Hedy edged nearer. 'Please. At least let us get our family back before you destroy magic.'

Lark actually looked remorseful. 'Even if it was the right thing to do, I . . . I don't think I *can* stop it now.' She eyed the growing emerald flames. 'One day you'll thank me, Hedy. All of you will. At least you have each other. The Hoarder Hill Four, you said. You'll find a new normal in life.'

Another powerful groan washed over the forest as the fire began to travel upwards hungrily.

Jelly suddenly huffed and dropped to one knee. Her skin was ashen, her eyes unfocused. 'Something's happening. I feel . . .' She fell to the forest floor, whimpering.

Another convulsion in magic was coming. Tempest squawked, her heavy brows lowered in pain.

The Spellbound Tree groaned again and this time the entire island quaked. All of them were thrown on to their backs. Ash, dirt, leaves went everywhere. The wave of topsy-turvy, breath-stealing force rippled outwards as the tree inched closer to its ruin.

Hedy rolled over to protect her face. A tingling sensation prickled at her skin and tugged her muscles. It wasn't the map. This was different.

When the tremor and the wailing wind finally eased, Hedy opened her eyes. Everything seemed different. She could see so much more to the sides and above in sharp focus, without having to move her head. The leaves of the forest seemed fantastically vivid; she could pick out shades of green she hadn't noticed before. Anxious bird calls from far away reached her ears. Right next to her, Tempest – immobilized, motionless as any ordinary stone carving – toppled to one side, making Hedy's whiskers twitch.

*Whiskers!* Hedy whipped her hands up to her face. They weren't hands, they were sharp-clawed paws. She brushed them against her whiskers, squeaking, and leapt lightly to her feet. She was around the same size as always but . . . furry. Brown and grey fur had sprouted from her elbows to her paws, and as she lifted her knees to inspect her legs – furry from the knees down with clawed feet at the ends – her bushy tail flicked out to help her balance.

*What am I?* she wanted to scream, but it came out as a frightened chitter.

Around her, other peculiar creatures were struggling up. A half-human figure with the freckly limbs of Spencer but the head of a large turtle, and a great turtle shell over its torso. Someone with a black rabbit's face and with a rabbit's hind legs, still wearing Jelly's sweatshirt. They'd all been turned into Theries: part-human, part-animal creatures that Hedy had only known to exist in paintings.

Beyond the rabbit Therie was a tiger. Hedy couldn't see any sign of human legs or arms on the beast, but as it twitched on the ground, a steel gauntlet slipped off its paw. Max.

In the other direction, closer to the tree, another Therie struggled to its feet. It had a pointed, brown, furry face with a collar of reddish fur around its neck and shoulders. Dark, leathery wings that spanned at least eight feet lifted from its back as it straightened to full height. The ripple in magic had transformed Lark into a bat Therie. Its face somehow resembled hers, the point of the chin and the shape of the eyes. Hedy shivered at the sight of her. At the point of those bat wings were human hands, and one of them clutched a snow globe.

The only creature that hadn't been changed was Chalky. He had retreated to a fallen tree trunk and looked this way and that, yipping in confusion at the uncanny beings that suddenly surrounded him.

'Chalky, it's OK,' Hedy tried to say to him. But her words were only insensible barks and he backed up further, wary of her.

Suddenly there was a growl to Hedy's other side. The tiger was up on its paws, tense with distrust. Hedy couldn't see any sign of Max in its eyes. It was like he'd been hit by the ripple in magic worse than the rest of them and had been transformed so fully that he didn't know them, or himself.

The animal part of her was instinctively terrified by him, cousin or not. *Predator*, Hedy's intuition said. *Get up high*. Safety in the high branches beckoned. She scurried up the nearest tree.

But the tiger wasn't interested in Hedy. Instead, he

leapt in the direction of the turtle Therie. Spencer snatched his head, arms and legs right inside his great shell, leaving nothing for Max to sink his teeth into. Frustrated, the tiger swung around and sprang for the rabbit Therie.

Jelly unthinkingly bounded away, high and fast, just out of reach. Max lunged for her again, jaws only millimetres from Jelly's rabbit foot, but out of nowhere two new strange Theries hurled themselves at him to knock him down. They were a stocky man with heavy shoulders and the head of a brown bear, and another lanky man with the head of a stag. Together, they completely overpowered Max and the bear man staunchly clamped the tiger's snout shut with his thick fingers.

'Young Max,' exclaimed the stag man, 'stop this foolishness. That's your sister.'

'And we're your friends,' rumbled the bear man. 'Don't you recognize Doug and Stan?'

'Why would he recognize us, you blockhead?' said Stan, pinning Max's hind legs. '*I* barely recognized you with that feeble body.'

'I've still got my handsome mug, and aren't your ridiculous antlers a giveaway?' Doug protested. 'Oi,

Max, no biteys!'

As they kept talking, Max stopped thrashing underneath them, his tiger aggression waning. Hedy almost cried with relief. She ached to jump down and hug her friends, but there wasn't time. She scampered along the bough, closer to the Spellbound Tree, and sprang down next to Chalky.

Whip-fast, Hedy swept the small creature into her paws. Chalky yowled and wriggled. He didn't know who she was. With his sharp teeth, he nipped her paw and Hedy squeezed her eyes shut in pain. Without warning, she was in Chalky's mind again. A great squirrel's face – *her face* – squeaking unintelligibly, clawed paws holding on so tightly and frightening him. She felt him take a breath and tense, gathering his green flame to make this creature let go. How could she get him to recognize her?

Suddenly Hedy remembered the game they'd played at Violette's apartment that had seemed to amuse Chalky so heartily. She brought an arm up to her eyes, and lowered it. *Peekaboo.* She tapped her nose twice and then lifted a paw to her ears. In her other paw, Chalky blinked at her, remembering the game. It bought her a moment's grace, enough to try something.

Focusing as hard as she could, she willed him to see her thought this time. A single image. Hedy the girl, not the squirrel, holding him.

He sniffed her, and relaxed. Recognition.

Lark screeched at them, a sound that was incomprehensible except for its note of warning menace. She held out a winged hand, glittering eyes boring into Hedy.

Hedy growled back and hugged the small chalkydri to her chest.

Lark shrieked again, and held Grandpa John's snow globe over the emerald flames at the root of the Spellbound Tree.

## CHAPTER 25

## THE FATE OF ALL MAGIC

Lark's threat was plain. Give Chalky to her, or she'd toss the snow globe on to the fire. A fire that could burn and destroy almost anything, Ines had said. Hedy didn't like the snow globe's chances against it.

And yet, she couldn't hand Chalky over to Lark. They had to get Chalky up to the heart of the tree and relight it. She could almost hear Grandpa John gruffly telling her not to be foolish, not to let the fate of one magician decide the fate of all magic. The responsibility to save magic had fallen to Hedy in his stead. And even before Lark's malevolent plans and bad luck had dragged them into this quest, Grandpa John had had faith in her to get it done.

Hedy shook her head defiantly.

Flaring her wings, Lark dropped the snow globe into the green fire eating at the Spellbound Tree.

Every reflex in Hedy screamed to dive forwards and save her grandfather, but that would put Chalky within Lark's reach. She battled the map and her very being, turned and scrambled away. Tears wet the fur of her cheeks. And that was when rain started to fall.

Mist at first, then actual raindrops, falling with a sizzle on the flames that had ascended the tree's trunk far too quickly.

Hedy and Chalky looked up. Above them through the forest canopy raced a cloud in the shape of a huge wolf, and peeking from its back were the faces of two Theries: a turtle and a rabbit. Together, Spencer and Jelly had given the cloud dragon a new shape and a new purpose: raining down on Chalky's fire. The wolf cloud shook itself like a wet dog. Water gifted from the naiad fell in fat drops, causing the flames to stutter and fizzle.

Lark shrieked and flapped her leathery wings to

take to the sky. She headed straight for the cloud wolf.

Hedy jumped uselessly into the air. She couldn't fly, she couldn't save her brother and her cousin. The only thing she could do was climb.

The smouldering bark of the Spellbound Tree sent excruciating pain through her padded paws as she picked her way upwards. Chalky clung obediently to her shoulder, twittering. Somewhere below her fur, the living map swirled in anticipation.

Twenty metres above the ground, Hedy finally reached the hollow in the heart of the tree. The map in her skin was begging her to go into it, but she didn't dare. Coaxing Chalky from her shoulder, she peered inside. It seemed as if an entire night's sky was within the Spellbound Tree. Immeasurable blackness, a sky that Hedy somehow knew should have been filled with stars, and which Lark wanted to stay empty for eternity.

Hedy chirped at Chalky and poured every ounce of will into sharing an image with him: the many-hued fire of the Ember Book. He pipped excitedly, and colours began to swirl through his fur again. She pointed into the hollow. Perched on the rim, the chalkydri opened his jaws eagerly and roared. Searing hot flame, all the colours of the rainbow and more, shot from his throat into the heart of the Spellbound Tree. It was a blazing wisp that quickly swirled down and away, a beam of the sun's fire speeding through the dying void.

Behind them, there was shouting but Hedy was only dimly aware of it. She was hypnotized by Chalky's flame spiralling away. Time slowed. And then – a flash. Spark after spark pulsing in the blackness. Glinting, flickering, glimmering. A chain reaction of something coming to life again. Faster, stronger, more brilliant, something was building. Chalky let out a satisfied hiccup of flame as a hundred suns freed themselves and burst upwards through the heart of the tree. Hedy reared back, her whiskers and face fur singed. Chalky had done it! He'd re-ignited the fountainhead of magic!

Hugging Chalky close with one paw, she steeled herself to descend the tree. She had a strong urge to turn upside down and scamper to the ground head first. But before she made a start, she was suddenly yanked by the tail. Head down, bottom up, she was dragged into the air in the grip of bat feet. Chalky squeaked and wriggled in Hedy's paw as Lark hauled them away.

Twisting her head, she saw the wolf cloud chasing them. But this time, Max in tiger form was snarling from its back. Behind him were the anxious turtle and rabbit faces of Spencer and Jelly.

Lark beat her leathery wings in a frenzy. The wolf cloud, however, seemed to have a supernatural tail-wind propelling it. Moment by moment, it closed the distance.

When they were a few metres away, the wolf cloud dived below Hedy. Spencer gestured at her with a tossing motion. Heart in her mouth, she threw Chalky to Spencer. The little chalkydri peeped as he sailed through the air, but Spencer caught him with sure hands. He beckoned to Hedy. *Jump!* But Lark's grip on her tail was like iron. She shooed her brother away, praying he'd understand they had to keep Chalky safe. With a despairing look, he nodded once and they sailed round to speed in the opposite direction.

Lark seemed to sense something going wrong. She wrenched Hedy forwards and, when she saw Hedy-squirrel was no longer holding Chalky, she immediately wheeled through the sky after the others. *She still wants Chalky*, Hedy realized, *still wants to use him to burn the Spellbound Tree.*

The furious beating of wings filled her ears – until Lark let go. Hedy flailed and screamed as she plummeted through the air. She wanted to close her eyes; they wouldn't stay shut. Something in her demanded she soak up her last moments before she hit the tree-tops and then the ground.

A wisp of something white dashed by the corner of her eye. *Thud.* The crash into the tree canopy never came. Instead, Hedy landed mid-air on something soft, white and a little damp. She sat up, breathless. Spencer and Jelly had sent a cloud offshoot to catch her. A wolf cub.

Higher up, Lark dived at the wolf cloud for Chalky, but Max – in his tiger form – impulsively leapt off it, right on to Lark's back. She staggered mid-air at his weight and his snarling jaws. They grappled and yowled in the air until Lark finally scrabbled free and flapped away as Max hurtled to the ground. Just in time, Hedy managed to manoeuvre her own wolf cub cloud beneath the tumbling tiger. He landed in the middle, sending up mist with his impact.

*Go!* she thought at her small wolf cloud and it started to heave away.

Wind lashed at Hedy's fur as they flew through the

sky. She squinted over her shoulder. Lark was in their wake, gaining metres as she beat her wings ferociously.

Something else was behind both of them, though. A black cloud of smoke, huge and fast-moving. It was moving in their direction. Was this something Jelly had created?

Hedy urged her cloud wolf cub to move faster. Onwards they flew, but with her next backwards look she knew the black smoke's pace outstripped theirs. Soon Hedy began to cough, feeling grit in her throat.

*Lark . . .*

The sound came from the smoke. A whisper so deafening that it would have been heard at either end of the isle in the stormiest of weather.

Hedy swung around and saw Lark reel in the air. The black smoke cloud grew even bigger and began to coalesce. Five colossal fingers opened up from a cavernous palm, reaching through the sky towards Lark. It brought a searing heat that sucked all the oxygen from them. In that moment, Lark's eyes looked utterly like that of the woman they had all thought her to be. She screamed. But the scream withered to an awful silence as the vast hand closed over her.

Hedy turned her cloud around and, choking, rode

her steed straight into the black smoke. The air sizzled as the dew of her wolf cub cooled the hot fumes. Her eyes stung like mad, her throat burnt like an inferno, but Hedy still tried to call out Lark's name.

There was no answer.

The sky lightened. Dark smoke curled and shrank away from Hedy and Max and began to scud back towards the Spellbound Tree, dissipating as it went. There was no Lark within it any more. Hedy rubbed the tears from her smarting eyes. In her paw was the wooden brooch, the tree with red berries that Lark had always had pinned to her cardigan. Nothing else was left of her.

Like a pack reuniting, the wolf clouds sailed across the sky, meeting at the Spellbound Tree. They descended through the trees until they were close enough to the ground for the peculiar group of Theries to tumble off safely.

Smoke was still thick here, but swirling in retreat towards the base of the Spellbound Tree. Through it, Hedy, Spencer, Jelly and Max heard two very welcome voices.

'Is that them?' said Stan.

'If it's that flaming bat traitor again, I'll give her what for,' growled Doug.

'Not if I get to her first.'

'*Pfft*, you leave the fighting to me, Stan. I know bats scare the pellets out of you.'

'What rot, Douglas. You're more full of droppings than a badger's latrine!'

Flailing to clear the smoke, Hedy finally saw Doug and Stan in their unfamiliar half-human forms. And beyond them, someone else. A man, stooping slightly, holding a gauntlet and a sword, and sagging to the earth in exhaustion. The black smoke cloud was receding to that sword, as though commanded by it.

Hedy's breath caught in her throat. More than anything, she wanted to call out, but she knew he wouldn't understand her squirrel noises. So she simply ran. With Spencer, Jelly and Max on her heels, she raced to the base of the Spellbound Tree and threw her paws around Grandpa John.

# CHAPTER 26

## SEEDLING

At midnight, somewhere over the narrow strip of Atlantic Ocean that separated France and England, a huge cloud materialized in the sky. It was shaped like a tall ship, and silently crossed the threshold from a place that very few people knew about, let alone had seen or visited.

Sailing the ship cloud was a motley group. Five people, four of whom had recently been part or wholly animal, and one of whom had lately woken from deep slumber. A talking bear rug. An equally garrulous stag's head. A stone gargoyle at the ship's prow, who flexed her shoulders, ready for battle should the need arise. And a small mythological creature of rippling rainbow colours.

As the cloud travelled away from the threshold, the Amazing John Sang waved the sword of a long-lost protector of the Spellbound Tree. Augmented by the sword's remaining power, the ripple of healing magic flowed outwards from the Spellbound Isle. It dispersed east across France and west across the United Kingdom. Before the witching hour was over, magicians in both countries had shed the Morpheus Web that had trapped them for days.

Less than an hour after that, the cloud passed over London. Places and things imbued with magic quietly came back to life: secret staircases, invisible inhabitants, objects with obscure histories. The British Museum that had disappeared so suddenly days before suddenly reappeared, along with the people who had vanished with it. Most of them weren't aware that time had passed, and asked each other, 'Why on earth is it so dark outside?'

The cloud ship slowed over the British Museum, but it was too risky to stop there with so many curious bogs stumbling out of the buildings. So it continued its journey and finally came to a halt over a house on a hill. It floated down, and let its riders disembark.

'Mrs Pal would be proud of you, Spencer,' said Stan as Spencer pulled him off the cloud.

'Too right,' said Doug. 'My, the wonders we've seen with you cubs.'

By the next morning, the whole family was reunited. Mum, Dad, Grandma Rose, Uncle Peter, Aunt Toni and Uncle Vincent drove back to Hoarder Hill as confused as everyone else who had been in the British Museum when it disappeared, although their suspicions were closer to the mark than others'.

Many fried eggs, slices of toast and cups of tea later, they had heard nearly everything about the children's fraught journey to the Spellbound Isle, and of Grandpa John finding himself released as Chalky's green fire burnt through the magical fetters of his snow globe. How he had sent the smoke cloud after the rogue former magician who had tried to destroy magic.

Spencer groaned. 'If only we'd known Chalky could've burnt away the Morpheus Web earlier!'

'How did you *know* Lark had gone rogue, Grandpa

John?' Hedy asked. She had a powerful craving for nuts and spread almond butter in a thick layer on her toast.

'The Woodspies,' said Grandpa John. 'She told me she had to use the bathroom but the Woodspies saw her trying to steal my Rosetta Jumbler. I ran to my study, but she unleashed the Morpheus Web on me before I had time to ward off the spell. The best I could do was turn it back on her as well. Do you remember that brooch of hers with the berries? It's made from rowan wood. Some believe that rowan wood protects against enchantment.'

'Smithy said the rogue magician's online username was Rowanberry,' said Jelly, slapping the table. 'I can't believe we didn't piece it together before she went all revengey.'

'I can't help feeling sorry for Lark,' said Hedy.

'Even though she dropped you from a height great enough to kill you?' exclaimed Stan.

Hedy nodded and squeezed on to Mum's lap for a hug, as though she were little. She hadn't been able to shake the image of Lark's eyes right before the vast hand of smoke had taken her.

'Well, in my opinion, the villain got exactly what she deserved,' rumbled Doug on the floor.

'What *actually* happened to Lark?' Spencer asked.

Grandpa John bowed his head. 'The vengeance of the Spellbound Tree itself took her. I created the smoke cloud to capture her, but the tree itself saw fit to punish her further. She is no more.'

A month later, the village of Marberry's Rest looked curiously out their windows and over their fences at all the visitors making their way to the house on Hoarder Hill. Grandpa John and Grandma Rose were opening their doors to the largest gathering ever to take place there.

The magicians of the Sleight came, of course – Candice, Flora, Morten and distant cousin Ewan Tsang. Ewan even brought his cockatoos, Chit and Chat, who flew up to roost upon the roof with Tempest and the other grotesques. They put up with Chalky following them like a pesky little brother. He was relishing his wings that had sprouted a fortnight ago, and decided Chit and Chat were somehow family due to their own ability to light up in the dark.

Mrs Pal, the maker who owned the Palisade magic shop, and her grandson Soumitra drove in. They were keen for Spencer to show them what he'd done to fix the skyskepnur, and to see it in action.

Mr Grutz entered the house as a welcome guest for the first time. He'd returned shortly after being released from a Paris jail with a hefty fine, but he hadn't spilt a single bean about Hedy and the others. He had turned a blind eye to Grandpa John using magic to repair all the damage to the house, and taken to saying hello over the fence rather than scowling at them. 'I'll be moving on soon,' he told them.

'Aren't we dangerous enough to warrant your attention any more?' Grandpa John asked, pretending to be miffed.

'No. I'd say you're getting a bit old and feeble for us to worry about,' said Mr Grutz, earning a laugh from Grandpa John, 'and anyway, I've got new fish to fry.'

Bess arrived through the Chinese lion slipway entrance in the garden with Violette. They even had Simon and his piano stool with them and regaled everyone with their trek into the catacombs to retrieve the ghost. Mrs Vilums and her sisters, freed from their stone forms, joined the gathering as well. In fact, everyone there was as they had been before. That included Grandpa John's poor health.

'Why couldn't the Spellbound Tree cure that too?'

Hedy had asked Grandpa John.

'Some things seem small but are beyond magic,' Grandpa John had replied. 'Besides, science is a magic of its own kind.'

Crowded in the secret room of the attic, the Sleight watched over Hedy, Spencer, Jelly and Max as they planted a seedling in a woodland clearing whose location was a mystery. It had been sprouted from one of the acorn-like nuts that the Spellbound Tree itself had shaken loose before they left its isle.

Candice said a few ceremonial words, and that was that. No traditions had ever been established for a rite such as planting a reserve Spellbound Tree. Everyone clapped, and then began to chat about which magicians' conclaves around the world should also be sent seedlings of the Spellbound Tree.

By the time everyone had got to the ground floor of the house, the children had disappeared.

Trying to keep quiet, Hedy, Spencer, Jelly and Max sneaked Doug, Stan and a cardboard box to the bottom of the back garden. Before long, Chalky joined them, having spotted them from the roof.

'Can we make cloud animals here and play tag?' Max asked.

'Maybe tomorrow,' said Jelly. 'If we don't go in before the big lunch, they'll send out the search party. Candice is dying to corner me about training for magic.'

In a sunny spot, beyond a garden bed wall, Hedy unpacked the cardboard box.

It was another seedling, one that they had held back from the Sleight for themselves. Using a small trowel they dug a hole. Hedy pulled Lark's wooden brooch from a pocket and placed it in the bottom of the hole with a pang of sorrow. Then they placed the seedling on top. Spencer waved his skyskepnur to create a small cloud in the shape of a bird, and with her bronze nail radiating, Jelly made it rain a little to water the seedling in.

'I wonder if it'll grow as big as *the* Spellbound Tree,' said Spencer.

Doug snorted. 'Be lucky if rabbits don't eat it before the day's out, more like.'

'I've got a warning for any hungry beasts,' said Spencer, waving his slingshot around. It was new, made from a Y-shaped branch that had fallen from the Spellbound Tree and that he had brought back. He hadn't done anything maker-ish to it, but its aim was surprisingly accurate.

'You could try rubbing your musk around here, Doug,' said Stan, 'and keep other animals from this territory of yours.'

'Musk? What am I, a polecat? Come to think of it, I don't know that it would be bad luck if this thing was eaten. Seems like something that could go wrong.'

'The Sleight aren't perfect at dodging trouble,' said Hedy. 'Couldn't the world do with a safety net tree? One that's off the grid?'

'You sound like Smithy,' Jelly snorted.

Max skipped around the grass. 'If it *does* grow really big, we should build a treehouse in it. Our headquarters. Oh, Jelly, you *have* to learn magic. And then find out from Beatrice how to make one of those magic forts that are teeny on the outside but like a castle on the inside.'

They talked for a long time, so long that they were late for the big lunch. But no one wanted to stop. Especially Hedy. They lay on Doug's back, wondering whether the seedling would one day somehow link to the Spellbound Isle. Whether wands could be made from its wood, or paper that would self-generate spellbinding stories to share with the world. Whether a treehouse among its branches might be able to travel through space or time. Whether animals that lived in it would develop special abilities. Whether Doug or Stan would regain their full bodies, or more, if they nibbled on the tree's leaves.

And every idea that spun from the one before it made Hedy smile and think, *Imagine that*.

## ACKNOWLEDGEMENTS

When we first started writing *The House on Hoarder Hill*, we were just hopeful to somehow have it published and for it to be read and enjoyed around the world. That quickly turned into an offer of writing a trilogy, securing literary and TV agents and a TV development deal. It's been quite a ride battling Theries, gargoyles, Mr Nobody, giants, sea kelpies and a few Hollywood lawyers but we are filled with gratitude for the whole experience.

Our thanks to these amazing teachers, students and schools:

Ms Canning, Charlie and St Bernadette's Catholic School, Coachella School district, Paige Middle School, Franklin Elementary, Cottonwood Elementary School,

Linda Walke & Yorke Mead Primary, Teresa Meredith & Loper Elementary, Lauren Alderman and Homebush Public School.

For being fantastic friends to us and the Hoarder Hill Four, we send big heart emojis to:

Mabel's Book Reviews and the Smith family, Matilda Bookmarks, Shoji, Barnes and Noble Palm Desert, Dan Baldwin, Damien Puckler, Shiloh Jiroudek, Lexi De Toth (for doing absolutely nothing), Dijanna Mulhearn, Heather Pretty, Anthony the Magic, Jim Hyde, Sean Webb, Mary Perry, Trixie Mauleon-Macro, Dede Grutz, Justin Nesseth, Heidi Gomes, Mary Liz Management, Katie Leffler, Kerry Davenport, Manuel Acosta, Ethan Copp, Puff Hatfield, The Frugal Frigate, Kendra Wester, Lia Brandligt, Naomi Watts, Susie Steadman, Tina Stripp, Candy Reesh, Kat Rallis, 'Adumb' Signorelli, Pingy & Pongy Latsch, Bookwagon UK, Julie Grasso and Middle Grade Mavens, Dre Horton for the hours of power, Joe and Claire Cocks, Eve and the Oppermann-Knopmans, Lia Quach, James and Bianca Abbotts, Malu Leicher, Lilli Lacher and Iris Lacher, and the Taday family.

Huge shout-out to the TV development team: Sam

Raimi, Zainab Azizi, Debbie Liebling, John Glenn, wiip and our agent Olivia Blaustein at CAA. Having other grown-ups get to know the universe of Hoarder Hill and want to explore its cloaked corners is an incredible feeling.

Awed thanks to all our book cover artists – Maxine Lee-Mackie, Petur Antonsson, Timo Grubing, Germain Barthélemy and Luis San Vincente. And we thank audio book narrators Harrie Dobby, Dan Bottomley and Fiona Hardingham for so beautifully bringing the books to life.

Love and gratitude to the OGs, Oliver and Paula Latsch of Latsch Literary Agency and Translations, for believing in us from the very start.

Thank you to our most extraordinary editor, Rachel Leyshon. When we're floundering around in the dark tunnels of story, Rachel is better than Chit and Chat at shining a light, better than Bess at identifying the treasure, more patient and skilled than Mrs Pal at helping us make something of it.

Huge thanks also to Laura Myers and Sue Cook for helping us make this book as watertight as can be.

We're grateful to the Chicken House and Scholastic teams for bringing Hoarder Hill to the world – Barry

Cunningham, Elinor Bagenal, Rachel Hickman, Jazz Bartlett Love, Sarah Wallis-Newman, Cassandra Rathbone and Samantha Palazzi.

Great thanks to our publishers worldwide, especially Catrin Abert and the Piper Verlag team.

From Kelly:

My love, kisses and bear hugs to:

Doug 'the Rug' Ngai and Kristen Cherrie for the laughs and cheering us on so loudly.

My parents, Juliana Ngai and Michael Ngai, the ultimate in love and support – and for fixing so many things.

Brent Armfield, who put up with me being lost in another world for so many early mornings and weekends, and always believes I can fight the foos.

Rufus and Xavier, for the questions, the answers, and making me want to write stories.

From Mikki:

Mikki's family – near and far!

Isabella Lish, Wendy, Jessica, Brandon Freeman, Julie and Rob Lawson, Zile & Vilums family and Agrita Krievina-Silins.

Uldis, Martins, Gint, Sharon, Amanda, Adrian, Thorley, Aleks, Josie, Annika, Ryan and Layla Silins for their unwavering support and love.

Colin Lish – for your West-Ham-sized love, support and belief in me. Your cheermaster talents for Kelly and me and especially for your love of cleaning our house!

And in loving memory of: Ilze Silins, Sandra Waizer, Jana Hale, Dianne Morton, Edward Stripp (I KNOW you are still critiquing my outfit choices!), Tom Grutz (whose 'gutz' I love & miss) and forever my funniest, most-loved friend, Doug Reesh.

Hoarder Hill gang – we will miss you. And hope to revisit you all again in the future.